THE PHILOSOPHY OF SCIENCE

AND

BELIEF IN GOD

The Philosophy of Science

and

Belief in God

Gordon H. Clark

The Trinity Foundation

Cover: Max Planck and Albert Einstein, 1929

The Philosophy of Science and Belief in God

Printed in the United States of America
ISBN: 0-940931-85-0

Contents

Books by Gordon H. Clark

Readings in Ethics (1940)
Selections from Hellenistic Philosophy (1940)
A History of Philosophy (coauthor, 1941)
A Christian Philosophy of Education (1946, 1988)
A Christian View of Men and Things (1952, 1991)
What Presbyterians Believe (1956)[1]
Thales to Dewey (1957, 1989)
Dewey (1960)[2]
Religion, Reason and Revelation (1961, 1995)
William James (1963)[2]
Karl Barth's Theological Method (1963)
The Philosophy of Science and Belief in God (1964, 1996)
What Do Presbyterians Believe? (1965, 1985)
Peter Speaks Today (1967)[3]
The Philosophy of Gordon H. Clark (1968)
Biblical Predestination (1969)[4]
Historiography: Secular and Religious (1971, 1994)
II Peter (1972)[3]
The Johannine Logos (1972, 1989)
Three Types of Religious Philosophy (1973, 1989)
First Corinthians (1975, 1991)
Colossians (1979, 1989)
Predestination in the Old Testament (1979)[4]
I and II Peter (1980)[3]
Language and Theology (1980, 1993)
First John (1980, 1992)
God's Hammer: The Bible and Its Critics (1982, 1995)
Behaviorism and Christianity (1982)
Faith and Saving Faith (1983, 1990)
In Defense of Theology (1984)
The Pastoral Epistles (1984)
The Biblical Doctrine of Man (1984, 1992)
The Trinity (1985, 1990)
Logic (1985, 1988)
Ephesians (1985)
Clark Speaks From The Grave (1986)
Logical Criticisms of Textual Criticism (1986, 1990)
First and Second Thessalonians (1986)
Predestination (1987)
The Atonement (1987, 1996)
The Incarnation (1988)
Today's Evangelism: Counterfeit or Genuine? (1990)
Essays on Ethics and Politics (1992)
Sanctification (1992)
New Heavens, New Earth (1993)
The Holy Spirit (1993)
An Introduction to Christian Philosophy (1993)
Lord God of Truth (1994)
William James and John Dewey (1995)
God and Evil (1996)[5]
Philippians (1996)

1. Revised as *What Do Presbyterians Believe?* (1965)
2. Combined as *William James and John Dewey* (1995)
3. Combined as *I & II Peter* (1980) and revised as *New Heavens, New Earth* (1993)
4. Combined as *Predestination* (1987)
5. A chapter from *Religion, Reason and Revelation*

Foreword

Christians and non-Christians alike commonly believe that science is an ever-growing body of knowledge about the universe. Scientific knowledge, according to this popular view, has been extracted from Nature with great difficulty–for Nature does not yield her secrets easily–by a group of extremely intelligent, highly educated, diligent, disinterested, and scrupulously honest men and women.

The progress of science, so this popular notion holds, can be seen in its glorious march from triumph to technological triumph. Just a century ago, powered flight a few feet above the Earth was thought to be impossible; in 1969 men landed on the Moon and returned to the Earth safely All the comforts and conveniences of the twentieth century are the fruit of science: indoor plumbing, abundant food, central heating and air conditioning, automobiles, television, computers, air travel, X-rays, and antibiotics–the list is almost endless. Science, it seems, has demonstrated its value and truth again and again.

To those who hold this popular and naive opinion of science, the argument of *The Philosophy of Science and Belief in God* will be quite startling. Dr. Clark carefully and fairly examines the belief that science furnishes us with truth, and then refutes it. His conclusion, please note, is not his alone, despite what the ordinary American–including many American

Christians–might think. But it seems that the views of many scientists and philosophers have not been as well publicized or as persuasive as the scientific inventions of the twentieth century.

In the modern mind there is a deeply rooted belief, not entirely traceable to John Dewey or William James, that success proves truth. Who can argue with success? Does not the sending of men to the Moon imply that scientists knew enough truth to get them there? Do not the longer life spans of Americans in the twentieth century prove that medical science knows more truth about nutrition and medical care than it did in the nineteenth century? If something works, is it not true?

Accompanying this popular notion of science as a body of truth is a widespread admiration and respect for famous scientists. Albert Einstein is probably the most famous and perhaps the most respected scientist of this century. But I doubt that many of his admirers know that he considered his own theories to be false, brilliant guesses, but not truth. In his biography of Einstein, Ronald W. Clark recounts a conversation between the famous physicist and Dr. Chaim Tschernowitz:

> Contemplation of first principles progressively occupied Einstein's attention. One visitor, Dr. Chaim Tschernowitz, has given a vivid account of a summer trip with him on the Havelsee during which their discussions were often metaphysical. "The conversation drifted back and forth from profundities about the nature of God, the universe, and man to questions of a lighter and more vivacious nature . . . ," he has written. "Suddenly [Einstein] lifted his head, looked upward at the clear skies, and said: 'We know nothing about it at all. All our knowledge is but the knowledge of schoolchildren.'
>
> " 'Do you think,' I asked, 'that we shall ever probe the secret?'

> 'Possibly,' he said with a movement of his shoulders, 'we shall know a little more than we do now. But the real nature of things, that we shall never know, never' " [*Einstein: The Life and Times,* Avon Books, 1971, 504].

This view of science as not furnishing truth has been argued at great length by other philosophers. For example, the British philosopher Karl Popper has written several books on the philosophy of science in which he argues that science, rather than consisting of a body of proven truths as many believe, consists of nothing but guesses and refuted guesses. Popper writes:

> First, although in science we do our best to find the truth, we are conscious of the fact that we can never be sure whether we have got it. . . . [W]e know that our scientific theories always remain hypotheses. . . . [I]n science there is no *"knowledge,"* in the sense in which Plato and Aristotle understood the word, in the sense which implies finality; in science, we never have sufficient reason for the belief that we have attained the truth. . . . Einstein declared that *his theory was false*–he said that it would be a better approximation to the truth than Newton's, but he gave reasons why he would not, even if all predictions came out right, regard it as a true theory [*Popper Selections,* edited by David Miller, Princeton University Press, 1985, 90, 91, 121; emphasis is Popper's].

In another book Popper has written:

> Our attempts to see and to find the truth are not final, but open to improvement; . . . our knowledge, our doctrine is conjectural; . . . it consists of guesses, of hypotheses,

> rather than of final and certain truths [*Conjectures and Refutations,* Harper and Row, 1968, 151].

To the predictable response that while scientific theories may not be true, they are at least highly probable, Popper (and Gordon Clark) respond: "It can even be shown that all theories, including the best, have the same probability, namely zero" *(Conjectures and Refutations,* 192).

What is the importance of all this? Why is it necessary to criticize a discipline that has bestowed so many obvious benefits on so many people and which is held in such high esteem? Well, it is not so much the discipline itself as popular misconceptions of the discipline that must be attacked. In the popular mind, science is the principal, if not the only, way to discover truth. It is precisely because science is held in such high esteem that it is necessary to remind people what it is. Zealous scientific evangelists like Jacob Bronowski, Julian Huxley, Ernst Haeckel, and Carl Sagan have proclaimed that science is the ultimate guide to truth; and they have chronicled the history of the warfare between science and Christianity. Because of the unflagging efforts of the scientific evangelists, "everybody knows" that Galileo was martyred for believing the Earth moves, and that Servetus–had Calvin not had him burned at the stake–would have discovered the circulation of the blood. In the popular mind, "It has been scientifically proved" has replaced the biblical formula "Thus says the Lord."

The Bible and science represent conflicting authorities, and it is the purpose of *The Philosophy of Science and Belief in God* to show that the popular beliefs about science are false. Were the limits and proper uses of science understood, there would be no need for this book. But since science has become an idol in the minds of many, its nature must be thoroughly discussed.

One of the problems of science is that it, unlike the Bible, is quite illogical. In his essay "Limitations of Scientific Method," the English mathematician, logician, and philosopher Bertrand Russell made the following observation:

> All inductive arguments in the last resort reduce themselves to the following form: "If this is true, that is true: now that is true, therefore this is true." This argument is, of course, formally fallacious. Suppose I were to say: "If bread is a stone and stones are nourishing, then this bread will nourish me; now this bread does nourish me; therefore it is a stone, and stones are nourishing." If I were to advance such an argument, I should certainly be thought foolish, yet it would not be fundamentally different from the argument upon which all scientific laws are based.

That is to say, all scientific laws are based on fallacious arguments.

Christianity, of course, is not dependent upon induction, experimentation, observation, or experience; its method is propositional revelation and rigorous deduction from the revealed propositions, for it is only through revelation that truth can be obtained.

In the sixth century before Christ, the Greek poet Xenophanes of Colophon understood the contrast between revelation and science, for he wrote:

> The gods did not reveal, from the beginning,
> All things to us; but in the course of time,
> Through seeking, men find that which is the better . . .
> These things are, we conjecture, like the truth.
> But as for certain truth, no man has known it,
> Nor will he know it; neither of the gods,
> Nor yet of all the things of which I speak.
> And even if by chance he were to utter
> The final truth, he would himself not know it:
> For all is but a woven web of guesses.

Like Xenophanes we affirm that apart from revelation, all is but a woven web of guesses. But we, unlike Xenophanes, have been given a revelation in the sixty-six books of the Old and New Testaments. It is these Scriptures, and only these Scriptures, not the methods of scientists, that give us truth. It is the Word of God that we must believe, not our own experience. Let us not abandon that Word, as Eve did in the Garden, because we see that science "is good for food, pleasing to the eyes, and desirable to make one wise." Science is false, and must always be false. Scripture is true and must always be true. The issue is as clear, and as simple, as that.

John W Robbins

Introduction

Various scientists and several philosophers have used scientific conclusions in an attack against religion. Some have denied the possibility of miracles but allowed the existence of God; others are completely naturalistic and rule out God altogether.

David Hume, for example, ruled out both miracles and God. He made an all-out attack on miracles, comparing the New Testament account of the resurrection of Christ with a fanciful rumor that Queen Elizabeth rose from the dead. Hume also left no room for God by proposing a cosmology in which the universe, instead of being a divine creation with a finite history, was pictured as an everlasting vegetable. Now, Hume was a philosopher, and philosophers who base their theories on scientific conclusions must not be ignored; but to judge them adequately it is wise first of all to examine the science and the scientists involved.

The theories of many scientists support Hume's view. Because the rejection of miracles has been so frequent and widespread, only one instance will be cited here. Austin Farrer, in his attack on orthodox Christianity, declares that it is scientifically *necessary* (italics his) to refuse to believe that the sun stood still for Joshua.* The larger issue between theism and

* Hans Werner Bartsch, ed., *Kerygma and Myth*, Harper & Brothers, 1961, 214-215.

atheism, however, is more important than the question of miracles; and several samples here of what will follow later are proper anticipations. From the alleged scientific conclusion of La Mettrie that there is no soul, Baron d'Holbach inferred that there is no God. Some years later Cabanis supported the denial of the soul by identifying thought as a physical secretion of the brain. The German scientist Büchner denied that thought was a secretion, but, identifying it as a motion of the brain, insisted on his atheism all the more vigorously: "Where there are three students of nature, there are two atheists." How science arrived at this position is a good part of the following story.

The theologians who reply to these attacks are under a disadvantage. When a scientist or a philosopher argues against religion, he does not need to know much about religion; but when a theologian discusses science, he must know quite a lot. The scientist can get by if he understands no more than that Christians believe God to be an incorporeal spirit; but the theologian is called upon to discuss space, time, motion, energy, electrodynamics, the solar system, quantum theory, relativity, and other assorted items.

There is something else the theologian must know, and something more important. In addition to a selection of particular pieces of information, such as the details just mentioned, the theologian must have an overall view of science as a whole. He must have a philosophy of science; that is, he must know what sicence is. Obviously he cannot compare, contrast, or relate religion and science unless he knows them both. This holds true for the scientist also. Perhaps the scientist can get by with a minimum knowledge of religion, but he surely ought to know what science is. Many scientists have an enormous amount of detailed technical information about electrodynamics and quantum theory, and yet lack an overall view–not merely an overall view of theology–but an overall view of science. Strange as it may seem, an accomplished artist often has little notion of what art is, and a man may be an expert scientist without knowing what science is. But any argument for or against religion, any argument that claims scientific support, depends more on the philosophic implications of science than on bits of detailed information. One must fit his science into a general philosophy. One must consider the range and the limitations of scientific application. One must know what science really is. Therefore, the major part of the present study, as it traces the history of science from older theistic constructions to more recent anti-religious positions, will be an attempt to say what science is: an attempt, in other words, to sketch a philosophy of science. Both the scientist and the theologian are invited to follow the argument, and it is not a foregone conclusion that the scientist will be more displeased than the theologian.

The philosophy of science is not a narrow and unimportant subject. Neither is religion. But to those who have not gone far into philosophy, science, or religion, another reason–more preliminary and superficial–may be given to stimulate sustained attention.

Our civilization in its dependence on telephones and television, on automobiles and jet planes, on modern merchandizing and UNIVAC, is permeated with science. Contemporary thinking, the thinking of non-scientists and non-theologians, is largely based on the scientific view of the world. The scientific method is said to be the best–indeed, the only–method for solving any problem, so that in every debate it is science, not theology, that has the last word. Since every curious and intelligent person naturally wishes to understand his own times, he must be prepared to give science sustained attention.

This is not easy. Contemporary science is extremely

complex. Yet it is not the obvious complexity, it is not the infinite accumulation of particular details, it is not the intricacy of advanced mathematics, nor even the extremely expensive equipment for putting a man in space that is the greatest and most important difficulty. The simplest things are the hardest. Nothing is more difficult to explain than the simple phenomenon of a marble rolling across a table. And it was one of the world's best modern scientists who admitted that he was completely baffled by the fact that when one picks up one end of a pencil, the other end comes along with it.

These simple problems are basic; therefore, they are very old. Men of other ages have wrestled with them. And in general it may be said that the superstructure of science in any age depends on how a marble is thought to roll or a stone to fall. Therefore, this monograph will divide the history of science into three chapters, corresponding to three scientific eras characterized largely by their divergent views as to how a body moves.

First, there will be a chapter on "Antiquity and Motion." Motion, just the plain fact that things move and change, is the basic and most universal scientific phenomenon. Its study was begun in Greece almost twenty-five hundred years ago; and since later thought, for all its boasted superiority, has relatively little more to offer on the main difficulty, the arguments may as well retain their ancient form.

Second, modern mechanism must be discussed. This is the empirico-mathematical physics that began with Galileo and developed without any serious break until the beginning of the twentieth century. Because of the commanding figure of Sir Isaac Newton, this may be called "Newtonian Science."

In the third place, some perplexing experiments were performed about the turn of the century. The changes in scientific theory that these experiments initiated proved to be far more revolutionary than at first suspected. Indeed, recent advances have left scientists gasping for breath. Things have become so disorganized and topsy-turvy that one is tempted to entitle the third chapter "Contemporary Confusion." But in order not to frighten the timid nor to prejudge the case before its hearing, we shall be content with the innocuous title, "The Twentieth Century."

Chapter One

Antiquity and Motion

Science, at least this chapter on science, begins with a study of motion. If there were no motion, there would be no science. Physics could exist in the absence of electricity, and zoology does not absolutely require butterflies. But neither can do without motion. Be it physics or zoology, the phenomena examined are either the causes and effects of motion, or the motions themselves.

Motion or change is an extremely familiar part of our experience. Plants grow and planets revolve. Hardly anything is more ordinary than a pencil or a ball rolling across a desk and falling off. Yet hardly anything is more difficult to explain. Most people simply take motion for granted and do not think about it. They never suppose that it needs to be explained. They fail to see that it presents any problem. The first aim of this section is to bring the difficulties to light. Just as a child whose daddy has always driven him around in a car may in his teens come to wonder how a car works and begin to study the principles of an internal combustion engine, so the college student, the scientist, and the theologian should cease to take motion for granted and begin to see that it presents some peculiar puzzles.

Zeno's Paradoxes

One of these puzzles was dressed up with great literary skill by an ancient Greek philosopher, Zeno the Eleatic (c. 450 B.C.). The story he told is so good that the reality of the intellectual puzzle is often missed in the fun. It is the story of the famous track race between Achilles and the tortoise.

One of Aesop's fables has a tortoise winning a race from a hare by reason of the hare's self-confident napping; but in Zeno's story, a much better story than Aesop's, the tortoise wins through sheer intelligence. The tortoise challenged Achilles to a race, and it was in the terms of the challenge that the brilliance was displayed. The terms were simple: The tortoise was to be given a head start of a certain distance, and Achilles was not to be considered the winner until he overtook the tortoise. Simple terms–deceptively simple. At the crack of Zeno's Eleatic pistol, the most famous track race of all history began. Now when Achilles, whose speed was legendary, arrived at the point from which the tortoise had started, the tortoise, quite obviously, was no longer there. During the interval, he had made some slow progress. Slow, no doubt; but progress nonetheless. Unlike Aesop's hare–for one thing, Achilles was not yet ahead of the tortoise–Achilles did not stop to take a nap; he kept right on running. Now, when Achilles by his legendary speed arrived at the point at which the tortoise was when Achilles had been at the point from which the tortoise started, the tortoise, quite obviously, was no longer there. During the interval, short as it was, he had made some small progress. Small, no doubt; but progress nonetheless. Achilles was still in no position to imitate Aesop's hare; he kept right on running. Now, when Achilles by his legendary speed arrived at the point at which the tortoise was when Achilles had been at the point from which the tortoise long ago had started, the tortoise, most obviously, was no longer there. During the interval, short as it was, he had made some small progress. Small, no doubt; but progress nonetheless. Well, this story, even without taking a nap at each juncture, begins to grow long. The upshot of the whole thing is that every time Achilles arrived at the point at which the tortoise had been, the tortoise was no longer there. Since now this happened every time, there was no time at which the ever-swift Achilles overtook the Eleatic tortoise.

Here most people laugh at the joke and thoughtlessly change the subject of conversation. Who is so stupid as to explain a joke? The question should be, Who is clever enough to explain this joke? Although over two thousand years have passed since Zeno told the story, even now no refutation of it commands universal assent. One of the superficial replies simply calculates how far Achilles runs in ten minutes (easily a mile) and how far the tortoise crawls in the same time (hardly a hundred feet). This elementary arithmetic shows that, if the tortoise originally had a lead of two or three hundred feet, Achilles is far ahead of the tortoise. This is superficial, and Zeno would not accept it because it presupposes a factor that Zeno does not admit. Of course, if Achilles could run for ten minutes, he would undoubtedly outdistance our slow but patient friend; but the brilliance of the tortoise in setting the original conditions by which he won the race depends on the fact that Zeno is not prepared to admit that Achilles can run for ten minutes. He is not prepared to admit that Achilles can run at all.

Stripping the puzzle of its literary embellishment, Zeno puts it point-blank. Consider a marble rolling across a desk, or, to be very scientific, consider an atom moving from one point to another in space. Before the moving body can reach the terminal point, it must obviously have traversed half of the distance. Surely, the body cannot reach the end before it passes the midpoint. But before it can reach the midpoint, it must have come to the quarter mark. And before this, it must have moved one-eighth of the distance, one-sixteenth, and so on. The "so on," however, is an infinite series, with the result that the moving body must exhaust an infinite series before it begins to move at all. Since, however, an infinite series is precisely a series that cannot be exhausted, it follows that a marble or an atom can never begin to move. Motion is impossible.

Therefore, Achilles never caught up with the tortoise.

The first reaction of a healthy American mind, a mind that has never taken much interest in intellectual activity and remains in undisciplined chaos, is to dismiss the whole thing as nonsense. Of course motion is possible! Why worry about it? Well, there is good reason to worry about it. Autos move too, don't they? At least, if there is a flaw in Zeno's argument, autos move. And it is the non-intellectual American, most of all, who thinks it worthwhile to study internal combustion engines. Now, if automotive engineering eventually requires a knowledge of mathematics, one should not stumble at the study of motion (atoms move, don't they?) just because it involves logic and infinite series.

Another superficial attempt to solve the problem depends on balancing off the infinite divisibility of the space against the infinite divisibility of the time. If Achilles must exhaust an infinite series of spaces, at least he has an infinite series of time in which to do it. This is plenty of time, and so he soon overtakes the tortoise. But this device merely doubles the problem. The difficulty of infinite divisibility will prevent time from starting as effectively as it prevented motion from starting. To avoid both of these difficulties–they are, as you see, exactly the same difficulty applied twice–Aristotle (*Physics,* VIII, 8) argued that the moving body does not actually pass through an infinite series of points. Zeno, says Aristotle, treats one point, the midpoint, as two. He takes it as both the end and the beginning of a motion. But this can be so only if the moving body stops at this point and then begins again. If the body is in continuous motion, none of these midpoints is "actualized." The points and the divisions are only potential and do not actually exist. Therefore, although it is impossible to pass through or exhaust an infinite number of actual points, there is no dfffìculty in passing through an infinite number of potential points.

If this solution arouses suspicion–and there does seem something queer about it, doesn't there?–perhaps Zeno's paradox is not so much nonsense as it first appeared. Possibly motion is indeed a little difficult to understand.

There is another attempt to answer Zeno. One may protest that since an infinite series does not have a last term, Zeno cannot require the moving body to reach the last term before it starts to move. He cannot erect as a barrier to motion a factor that admittedly does not exist. And yet, did Zeno say that it was necessary to reach the last term? Will not his paradox remain if he simply asserts that motion cannot begin so long as there are more terms in the series? This is long enough.

Well, perhaps a slightly different expedient will allow the body to move. Let us grant that in any finite space an infinite number of points actually exist. Let us also grant that to move from here to there a body must pass through *all* of these points. But let us deny that the body must pass through *each* of these points. That is, we claim, Zeno confused a *collective* all with a *distributive* each. He supposed, mistakenly, that whatever is true of one must be true of the other. Yet there are many examples where the collective all has qualities quite different from the distributive each. Each nail in this keg is easy to pick up but it is difficult to pick up all of them. Similarly, what is true in every case is not necessarily true in general. Aristotle argues that although a theorem be proved for each of the three types of triangle, it has not on that account been proved of triangle generally. Or, finally, each element of a compound may be poisonous (NaCl), but the whole may be good to eat. Zeno, therefore, was mistaken because he insisted that a moving body must pass every point, when as a matter of fact, it need only pass all of them.

Is this solution suspicious too? Let us be careful. There are not many more solutions, and if we cannot decide on one of them, we may be forced to conclude that motion is impossible. And where would science be then, poor thing?

The Heraclitean Flux

Since we cannot stop here for another two thousand years to work out better replies to Zeno, we must proceed as if these objections had never been raised. Let us banish them from our memory. Let us resolve not to think about them. We must without further ado simply assume that things are in motion. One of the first philosophers to study motion, indeed the very first philosopher to make motion the main object of his study, concluded, not only that things are in motion, but that all things are in constant motion.

The slogan of Heraclitus (c. 500 B.C.) was, "All things flow." He likened the universe to a river with new waters continually succeeding upon the previous waters. Nothing remains at rest; everything changes. Therefore one cannot step into the same river twice. If the river consists of the water, and the water is never the same, then the river is never the same; so that no one can step into the same river twice. If an attempt is made to avoid this conclusion by pressing the illustration and if it is remarked that a river has bed and banks as well as water, Heraclitus would reply that the bed and banks are being constantly eroded and never remain the same. Even the tiniest visible pebble or particle of sand is constantly changing. Nothing remains the same.

There is also another reason why a man cannot step into the same river twice. Not only does the river change, but the person changes also. Nothing of the man remains the same; so that at the two times of stepping it would not be the same man.

Although Heraclitus was an ancient Greek, the universality of motion is not a strange idea in modern times. Atoms used to be considered as internally stable and solid, but with the splitting of the atom there has come a view that the atom is somewhat like a miniature solar system whose parts revolve around a central nucleus. Still further, the nucleus of the new atom and its satellites are not usually regarded as solid pellets; but the whole stuff of the universe is supposed to be a sort of palpitating field of energy in which nothing is stable. Undoubtedly, modern scientists and contemporary philosophers differ on several details and even on major questions; but the idea of universal change is at least not strange in our present era. For that reason the implications which Heraclitus and his disciples drew from their view that all things flow are considerations which must be kept in mind even today.

It was Kratylus, a disciple, rather than Heraclitus, who drew some of these conclusions. Our chief interest here is, of course, the analysis of the concept of universal change and not the precise historical development. The question therefore is: If all things change, if nothing remains at rest, what follows?

Plato comments caustically that the Heracliteans exemplify their principle in that their opinions never remain the same. They never answer the same question twice in the same way. Their minds flow as constantly as their river. Kratylus, however, was able to escape Plato's charge. Whenever he was asked a question, no matter what the question was, he always gave the same answer. Only the answer was not in words but was a waving of the hand.

Perhaps Kratylus was consistent; perhaps the theory of universal motion makes intelligible speech impossible. Let us see. If the river is constantly changing, can it be called a river at all? When we call a thing a river, or even a cloud, we believe that it remains a river or a cloud for some space of time. Rivers presumably last longer than clouds; but even a cloud, to be called such, must last long enough to be recognized and named. Something about it, at least something, must remain the same and not change, or else it would not be-what we name it. This is not to say that the river must remain unchanged in every respect; nor is it to say that it must remain unchanged in any respect forever, but unless something (its being a river) does not change into something else (its not being a river) the name would have no meaning. Hence the possibility of intelligible speech presupposes the existence of entities that remain unchanged for some finite time, and conversely the theory of universal change makes speech and knowledge impossible.

In the *Timeaus,* Plato has produced a good illustration of this point. He supposes that a skillful sculptor is modeling a statue in gold. Gold is soft and malleable and can be worked quickly. For the illustrative purpose we may speed up the process to emphasize the point. The sculptor, now, models a statue of Zeus, and one of the onlookers asks you what it is. But the sculptor does not stop modeling the moment Zeus appears in the gold; he continues with steady speed. And before you can say Zeus, it isn't Zeus any more. Perhaps it begins to take the shape of Socrates, or of a centaur. Each time, however, that you think it safe to call it something, it has already changed. It is not something; it is nothing.

Of course, one might say it is gold. It may not be Zeus or a centaur, but it is surely something, and that is gold. In answer to this reply we shall have to develop Plato's implications a bit further than the explicit illustration. We are tempted to call it gold, are we not, because the gold as gold remains unchanged throughout the process. But suppose again that the gold did not remain gold. Suppose that during the modeling process the gold itself was changing into clay. Suppose, too, that as soon as it seemed to be almost clay it began to change into wax. Under such conditions how can we answer the question, what is it? Not only is it not Zeus; it is not gold, it is not clay, it is not wax, it is not anything. That is to say, if a thing is changing, it does not exist; or, to generalize, if everything is changing, nothing exists. Universal change implies universal non-existence. And this implies that the changing is unreal and reality is unchanging.

Why, this sounds like Zeno all over again! Have we once more shown that motion is impossible?

Aristotelianism

The climax of antiquity's study of motion is found in Aristotle. Before the more intricate parts of his theory are examined, the immediate reply to Heraclitus will serve as an easy starting point. Aristotle agrees that if everything were always changing, nothing would exist and knowledge would be impossible. Therefore, he concludes, something must exist that does not change.

The assertion that something exists unchanged, at least for a finite period of time, does not depend solely on Aristotle's desire to support the possibility of knowledge, though the possibility of knowledge is, of course, a highly important matter. But the existence of something unchanged is also directly connected with the possibility of motion itself. That is to say, in order that something may move, something must remain unmoved. The situation in which motion takes place is a little complicated. When we express an instance of motion or change, we say the green leaf turned brown, or the uneducated boy became an educated man, or, merely, the marble rolled from here to there. In every case something must remain unchanged during the change. A leaf can turn brown only if it is the same leaf at both ends of the change; a marble rolls from here to there only if it is the same marble all the time.

Suppose it were not the same leaf and the same marble. Then we would have seen a green leaf and a little later a brown leaf; but there would have been no change, for nothing would have changed from green to brown. Or a magician might deceive me by substituting a second marble for the first and so produce an illusion of motion. But if there are two marbles, neither of them rolled from here to there. The first one did not roll because it did not arrive there. The second one did not roll, because it did not begin here. All motion, therefore, requires a subject that remains unchanged during the motion.

A modern invention provides a better illustration than Aristotle ever thought of. In the movies there is no image that moves. The motion is all an illusion. We think we see the picture of a man walking across the background. But we know that there are some sixteen pictures being projected on the screen every second. One of the pictures appears on the screen in a definite and fixed position. It cannot move. The next picture then replaces the first, but in a very slightly different place. The whole process is one of substituting another image for the preceding. The resultant motion is an optical illusion, for there is nothing that moves. Motion, then, presupposes an unchanged substratum.

Yet there is a question. Motion, no doubt, presupposes an unchanged substratum, but how do we know there is such a substratum and how do we know there is motion? Perhaps the motion picture screen is a good illustration of the world. Why should we assume that there is a substratum before our eyes outside the theater any more than inside? Even some Christian theologians, surprisingly enough, have advanced a theory called continuous creation. They suppose that God is constantly creating; the world cannot preserve itself and is constantly collapsing; God at every moment recreates it. Some of these theologians do not press the wording very far, but a few seem to mean that a new world replaces the preceding, sixteen or sixteen hundred times a second. In this case there would be nothing that could move; each thing would exist momentarily at a fixed point. Now, why cannot this be the truth? Is there any evidence, any compelling evidence, that something remains unchanged for any finite period of time?

Perhaps, however, we are wrong in expecting too much from Aristotle's simple repudiation of the Heraclitean flux. He has other and much more profound arguments to give. These intricate theories may be more easily grasped if they are prefaced by a short account of the contrasting views of Democritus. Democritus was an atomist and a mechanist. He spent no time on Zeno's paradoxes and was only indirectly influenced by the philosophy of Heraclitus; he simply started with the assumption that atoms move in empty space. For him, therefore, motion is an indemonstrable axiom, an inexplicable brute fact. But though motion as such cannot be explained, every particular motion can be. Just as, on a preceding page, someone tried to say that a moving body could pass all the points but could not pass each point, so here Democritus will explain each motion but not all. Select any atom you like, and its motion, speed, and direction can be explained by the force and angle of impact of another moving atom. This other moving atom had in its previous turn been struck by another atom, and so on back *ad infinitum.* Motion never began; it had no original source; it will never end; it is an ultimate brute fact.

Aristotle, on the other hand, believed it possible to explain not only every particular motion, but also motion in general. In doing so he rejected the philosophy of mechanism and with it the atomistic picture of the world. Instead of mechanism, he defended teleology. Instead of atoms in an infinite void, he assumed a completely filled finite world. The resulting view is difficult to understand, though it is not for this reason to be supposed untenable. The principle of mechanism is, of course, very easy to grasp, even if with Aristotle one finally concludes that it fails. There is nothing to do, then, but to study the arguments in as much detail and with as much thoroughness as our interest permits.

One cannot object to Democritus on the ground that he made certain indemonstrable assumptions. Every philosopher and every system of philosophy must start somewhere, and obviously nothing can be prior to the starting point. For Aristotle, however, the starting point is not the fact of observed motion, but the existence of nature. "*That* nature exists," writes Aristotle *(Physics,* II, 1), "it would be absurd to try to prove; for it is obvious that there are many things of this kind [natural objects], and to prove what is obvious by what is not is the mark of a man who is unable to distinguish what is self-evident from what is not."

Now, Aristotle's import is not quite so simple and obvious as it seems. One may indeed suppose that natural objects, such as trees and rocks, are at least as self-evident as motion. In fact, since motion is always the motion of some such objects, since therefore the objects are logically prior to the motion, why is it not better to begin with them rather than with it?

Such a consideration, however, is not a great support to Aristotle's procedure, for although many people would be inclined to say that nature consists of these objects–trees, rocks, animals, earth, air, fire, and water–this is not Aristotle's definition of nature. These objects are natural, they have a nature, they act according to nature, but it is not true that they are nature. Nature, for Aristotle, is a principle of rest and motion, immanent in these bodies per se. How nature is the cause of rest may be deferred for a moment; for the present it is to be noted that nature is not an object, like a tree or a rock, nor even the aggregate of them, but a principle of motion in the object. Democritus had located the cause of every motion in a body other than the one whose motion he was explaining; the cause of any motion is always external to the body which is the subject of that motion. But for Aristotle, the cause of motion is immanent in the moving body itself. To be sure, Aristotle acknowledges forced or unnatural motions that are caused by impact. When a stone is thrown upward, the cause is the hand and arm that threw it. But this is an unnatural or violent motion. However, the fall of the stone is natural, just as natural as the growth of a plant; and the cause of a natural motion is not an impact from without but an immanent principle in the moving body itself. It is the nature of that body.

Now, it is to be wondered whether such an immanent principle of motion is as obvious and self-evident as either the object or the motion itself. If we rely on sensation, we may say we see and know immediately that things move. But can it be maintained that an immanent cause of motion is immediately known? No doubt, something must be a self-evident indemonstrable starting point; but is it self-evident that natural motion cannot be explained by collision and impact? Perhaps, however, *self-evident* does not mean immediately perceived. Perhaps there is a complicated argument to show that the mechanical theory of motion is unsatisfactory. Perhaps, further, all attempts fail except Aristotle's, and his first principle succeeds in solving the problem. Then we might say that it is necessary to start with nature conceived as an immanent principle of motion and rest.

Nature then would be self-evident in a very sophisticated sense of the term, but only a careful analysis of the argument can justify such a conclusion.

In the *Physics,* Book III, Aristotle begins a determined attack on the problem of motion. He spares no effort to arrive at a solution. And effort is required, for the explanation of motion must make use of the concepts of continuity, infinity, place, time, and perhaps void. This is a constant trouble with philosophic subjects. One hardly begins a topic before one discovers that another matter calls for prior attention. We are always being pushed back or forward, until it seems impossible to solve any one problem without solving all. Omniscience is the prerequisite, and omniscience is hard to come by. But Aristotle makes a brave beginning.

First, he must define *motion.* When one undertakes to discuss a matter, it is advantageous to know what the subject of conversation is. In the early Platonic dialogues, Socrates was able to tie his opponents in knots because they did not know what they were talking about. Protagoras could not define *virtue,* Euthyphro could not define *piety,* and Laches, although he was a general of the army, did not know what *courage* was. Similarly, the pre-Socratics had failed to unravel the enigma of motion, chiefly because they did not know what *motion* is. Their halting hints were faulty as definitions. Within this section *(Physics,* III, 1) Aristotle formulates the definition of *motion* three times. First, he says that motion is the actualization–literally, he says the actuality–of the potential *qua* potential. This cryptic phrase is then explained. When that which is buildable, insofar as it is buildable, is actual, it is being built; and this is the motion or change called building. Note that the completed house is not buildable; it is built, and the motion is completed. Nor is the actuality of brick and wood motion; insofar as the materials as such are concerned, the motion has not yet begun. This motion, therefore, is the actualization of the buildable *qua* buildable.

Aristotle must insist on the importance of the *insofar as*, the *qua*, the *as such*. Bronze is potentially a statue, but the actuality of bronze *qua* bronze is neither a statue nor motion. To be bronze and to be movable do not mean the same thing. Or, again, to be potentially healthy is not the same as to be potentially sick; for, if it were, to be actually healthy would be to be actually sick. Of course the same person may be sick or well, but the potentialities are different. Motion then is the actualization of the potential *qua* potential.

The second time Aristotle formulates the definition he says, "Motion is the actuality of a potential being when it operates in actuality not insofar as it is itself, but insofar as it is movable." The third formulation, a few lines below, is essentially a repetition of the first.

Now, the second of these three formulations is clearly untenable: It is obviously circular. To define motion as the actuality of the movable is to use the concept of motion in its own definition. How could one know what *movable* means, *i.e.*, able to move, unless one first understood motion? This circularity is present also in the example given under the first formulation. What *buildable* means cannot be known until the motions of building are understood. Either then Aristotle has made a circular blunder, or the first and third formulations must somehow escape this criticism.

It is not at all certain that the second formulation is a mere slip of the pen which is excusable in the light of the other two. In *Physics*, VIII, 1 (251a8), a passage presumably referring to *Physics*, III, 1, Aristotle again defines motion as the actuality of the movable *qua* movable. Similarly, a few pages later (257b8) he says, "Motion is an incomplete actuality of the movable." It would seem therefore that the taint of circularity is more than merely superficial.

However, Aristotle should be given every opportunity to rebut this charge before a final judgment is entered. Since, then, he furnished two other formulations, these also should be examined. And, it must be admitted, they contain at least no apparent circularity. Motion is the actualization of the potential *qua* potential. It is requisite, however, to state what is meant by the term *potential.* In fact, two requirements must be met. First, the term *potential* must be defined without using the idea of motion, or else the circularity will reappear, and, second, the idea of potentiality must be set forth clearly and unambiguously, or else all physics will remain vague and confused.

The clarification of the concept of potentiality is found more in the *Metaphysics* than in the discussions on motion. In Book Delta Aristotle says, "Potentiality is a source of motion and change which is in another thing than the thing moved or in the same thing *qua* other. . . . Potentiality then means the source of change or motion. . . ." It would seem, however, that this is not altogether satisfactory. In the *Physics* Aristotle defined *motion* in terms of potentiality, and now in the *Metaphysics* he is defining *potentiality* in terms of motion. Circularity, therefore, has not been avoided, and we still do not know what motion is.

There is, however, another passage. In Book Theta of the *Metaphysics* (1048a30-b6) Aristotle defines actuality. "Actuality means the existence of an object, but not in the manner we call potentiality. We say, for instance, that a statue of Hermes is potentially in the block of wood . . . because it can be cut out of it. We also call a man a scholar even when he is not studying, if he is actually capable of studying. . . . We must not seek a definition of everything, but be content to grasp an analogy: that as he who is building is to him who can build, and as he who is awake is to him who is asleep, and as he who sees is to him who, though not blind, has his eyes shut . . . so actuality is defined by one member of these antitheses and potentiality by the other."

Even in this more extended passage it is a question whether circularity has been avoided. Cutting the statue out of wood, studying, and seeing are motions; and thus potentiality and actuality are explained on the basis of motion. Motion, then, cannot properly be defined in terms of potentiality.

But, says Aristotle, this is not a definition. Potentiality cannot be defined. It must be grasped by analogy. As he who is asleep is to him who is awake, so potentiality is to actuality. Now, the man who is asleep is horizontal, and the man who is awake is vertical. Is this what Aristotle means? Of course not. But it is hard to tell what he means, for there are many comparisons that can be made between men asleep and men awake. The former dream; the latter do not. How can one select which point of comparison is intended? It would seem, therefore, that even if Aristotle has avoided the apparent circularity, he has not given us a clear and unambiguous concept of potentiality.

The ambiguity of potentiality and the uselessness of analogies become clearer when Aristotle turns from motion to consider the infinite as a potentiality. The subject concerns the infinite divisibility of lines and the never-ending possibility of addition. Infinity, by his argument, is something potential, not actual, because it can never be completed. Now there is some sense in calling a block of wood a potential statue because it can be chiseled into one. But a block of wood could hardly be called a potential spark plug or a potential magnet, for these cannot be made of wood. To show that an object is potentially something, it is necessary to show that on some occasion or other it has become that something. The criterion of potentiality, therefore, is an instance of its having become actual. But here in the discussion of infinity Aristotle says, "The infinite is potential. But potentiality must not be taken in the sense that wood is a potential statue, that is, it will be a statue, as if there were an infinite that would later become actual. But as being has several meanings . . . so also does the infinite" (206a17-23). And, we must add, so also does the potential.

Here then is another sense of potentiality, not clearly related to the analogy of sleeping and waking. What can be made of it? To be told that it is a sense different from the preceding, when the preceding is itself all too vague, is not a sufficient explanation to serve as the basis for solving the problems of motion.*

This argument may now seem to have become all too intricate. The interest of the reader may have dissipated along the way. But the conclusion should be disturbing enough to jolt him out of any tendency to doze. The conclusion is not that Aristotle got himself into a jam; such would be merely a piece of historical information. Nor is the conclusion simply the meaninglessness of the concept of potentiality and the uselessness of analogical definitions. Such is, of course, a valuable warning to any ambitious philosophers who are unknowingly starting up a blind alley. But there is a much more disturbing conclusion than all this. It is that the problem of motion remains unsolved.

This failure is even more catastrophic than a failure merely to decide whether motion depends on a spontaneous, internal principle or an external impact. We are not permitted to reject Aristotle and fall back on motion as an observed brute fact. The analysis has annihilated Democritus as well as Aristotle. The

* To complicate the matter still more, consider the argument of 206b20 ff. Aristotle contends that infinite magnitude cannot exist even potentially because there is no actual infinite. Here the non-existence of an actuality is taken to prove the non-existence of a potentiality. This works well enough in the usual case of the statue, but, if this interpretation is correct, it makes the second sense totally impossible.

reason is that we do not know what motion is. We have no concept of motion. We have nothing clearly in mind when we use the word. We simply do not know what we are talking about. And in the recesses of our oblivion there still lurks the skeleton of Zeno's Achilles. Perhaps motion, and science along with it, is just nonsense.

CHAPTER TWO

NEWTONIAN SCIENCE

One of the best-publicized boasts of modern civilization is its superiority over Medievalism in science. The Middle Ages were times of ignorance, superstition, and scientific sterility. Not to mention the relics of the saints, the whole lumber yard of fragments from the true cross, and such forgeries as the Donation of Constantine and Dionysius the Areopagite, ignorance in physics is evident in the low level of material culture and bodily comfort. In this regard, the Middle Ages were inferior even to antiquity for their best men had little understanding of or control over natural processes.

On the other hand, modern times are superior beyond comparison. Knowledge, discoveries, and inventions have come in startling profusion. Quite obviously the construction of this new civilization, even the first step of this construction, was an advance of the first order. What explains it? Let us not think that the men of the Renaissance, who laid the foundations of such achievements, had more brain power than the ancients and the scholastics. Aristarchus, Archimedes, and Ptolemy were brilliant scientists; and the Medieval scholars, few though they were in number, and more metaphysical than scientific, were extremely acute. The difference depends rather on the problems attempted and the methods used.

Medieval chemists, alchemists they were called, chose as their main problem the reduction of baser metals to gold. The problem can be and has been solved, but it is one of the most difficult physico-chemical problems imaginable. None could have been a worse problem with which to begin chemistry. The methods of the Middle Ages were utterly unable to cope with it. In fact, the scientific methodology of the Middle Ages could cope with very little. It was the Renaissance, the new birth of knowledge, that discovered what we now familiarly call the scientific method; and the eventual purpose of this discussion is to state, explain, and analyze this method; for science and the scientific method are the dominant intellectual interest of modem times and the basis of our civilization.

One of the more obvious differences between Medieval and modern method, and even between ancient and modern interest, was the sloughing off of fanciful and useless sophistries. This new generation paid no attention to silly puzzles about Achilles and the tortoise. They neither cared to prove that motion occurs nor would they waste time on futile definitions or explanations of motion in general. Aristotle had not only defined motion, but he had also given a careful account of time. But Sir Isaac Newton said, "I do not define *time, space, place,* and *motion,* as being well known to all." Putting all sterile sophistry behind them, they set about a direct investigation of nature. The result is that today instead of ignorance and illiteracy, open fireplaces and the black death, swords, arrows, and horses, we have universal education, central heating (except in London), wonder drugs, hydrogen bombs, and jet planes. Such is the triumph of modern science over Medievalism.

Flaws in Aristotle

Now, for all the darkness of the Dark Ages, we must not suppose that no serious studies of natural phenomena were made. A modern superstition is that the Medieval scientists thought the earth was flat. Boasting and superiority should be tempered by correct historical information. Without detracting one whit from the fame and genius of Sir Isaac Newton, we should acknowledge that certain flaws in Aristotle's account of motion stimulated Medieval thinkers to think. There were at least two very real problems that men before the time of Galileo were seriously studying. One was the motion of projectiles; the other was the similar problem of a freely falling body.

According to Aristotle, every body that is set in motion is set in motion by a mover that exerts force on it. This is particularly evident in the case of a stone's being thrown upward. It cannot move itself; it must be moved by something else. In fact, since upward motion is unnatural for a stone–by nature stones fall downwards–force must be exerted on the stone at every moment of its ascent; otherwise it would start to fall. But what exerts the force? The hand that threw the stone, and, to take a Renaissance example, the explosion that first propelled a cannonball, is no longer in contact with it. And is it not obvious, perfectly obvious, that one body cannot exert force on another body without being in contact with it? A hand cannot throw a stone it does not hold; nor can one billiard ball set another in motion except by impact. How then can the stone continue to go up after it has left the hand?

The Aristotelian answer, interpreted and expanded from the none-too-clear passage of *Mechanica* (858a19, 30), is that when the hand first pushes the stone up, the stone pushes away the air above it; when the stone leaves the hand, the displaced air rushes in behind the stone and pushes it still higher; this displaces more air, and so the stone continues its flight.

Related to the phenomena of projectiles, the second problem to engage the late Medieval thinkers was the motion of a freely falling body. This is, it would seem, a more complicated problem. So far as projectiles are concerned, one need only explain how they continue in motion; but a freely falling body not only continues in motion–it accelerates. Indeed the most obvious fact about a falling body is that its motion is much faster near the end of its fall than it was at the beginning. Now, inasmuch as velocity, on Aristotelian principles, is proportional to the force exerted, a constant force would produce a uniform motion, not an acceleration. A falling body, then, must be subject to a constantly increasing force. How is this to be explained? What makes a falling body fall faster?

These are two conspicuous difficulties in the Aristotelian system. Now, when such particular points of difficulty are found–whether embedded in the Aristotelian, the Newtonian, or any other system–the normal procedure is to try to work out the puzzle within the framework of the accepted system. This is only common sense. A body of science is not to be discarded *in toto* just because a minor point presents a difficulty. But sometimes, once in three or four or fifteen centuries, the supposedly minor point reveals such a basic flaw that a completely new construction is called for. Such happened to be the case in this instance.

The Aristotelian theory of nature, which concerned itself also with forms of change other than locomotion–with alteration and growth for example–was teleological and organic rather than mathematical and mechanistic. The causes of change were sought in the qualities rather than in the quantities of body. Animals in natural motion are moved by their souls or inherent forms. In one place, Aristotle explains why some trees produce sweet fruit.

> Trees which grow in sour water produce sweet fruit because the sourness assisted by the heat of the sun

> attracts that which is of its own quality, namely, cold and dryness. Sweet liquids therefore make their appearance inside the tree . . . *(De Plantis,* 829b).

Qualitative explanation applies to locomotion also: Stones fall because they are heavy, and fire ascends because it is light.

Often the qualities that produce the effects are not evident. Drugs and chemicals produce their effects, to talk in Medieval language, by reason of occult qualities, that is, qualities that are hidden from view. But to say that opium causes sleep by reason of its dormitive or soporific quality is to cover one's naked ignorance with vaporous verbiage. Aristotle's teleological theory of nature, therefore, is credited with the sterility of Medieval science.

Now, to return to the question of locomotion: The use of some modern terminology will the most easily identify certain confusions in Aristotle's thought. In spite of the risk of anachronism one can hardly avoid using modern terminology because the conceptual framework of Aristotle's theory (see *Physics,* VIII) is so foreign to the modern mold of mind that our difficulty is no longer that of refutation, but of mere understanding. With some lack of precision, therefore, it will perhaps suffice to suggest that for one thing Aristotle confused what we consider to be the two distinct concepts of velocity and work; and for another thing, his merging of size and force prevented him from attaining what we would call a clear definition of the latter. And this returns us to the question, What force makes a projectile continue to move?

In the middle of the fourteenth century, a philosopher by the name of Buridan made a very remarkable suggestion. He supposed that when the stone was put in motion by the hand, the very fact of its moving, while in contact with the hand, produced a new quality in the stone. This new quality he called impetus. Everyone has observed that when iron is heated in the fire, it remains red for a time after it is withdrawn from the fire. It does not become black again instantaneously. Why, then, may not the hand by its motion impart an impetus to the stone so that the stone will continue to move for a time after contact has ceased?*

Later, toward the end of the sixteenth century, Galileo took a further step and formulated an interesting argument that contributed to the replacement of Aristotelianism by modern mechanics. He noted that after a pendulum descends through one half of its arc, it rises on the other side of the perpendicular to the same height from which its swing began. And again, if a marble is allowed to roll down an inclined plane and at the bottom meets and must roll up another incline, it will rise to the level from which it started. On the basis of such observations, Galileo constructed an ingenious argument. During the descent, the marble or pendulum accelerates; during the ascent. it decelerates. Therefore, Galileo concluded, at the bottom of the descent, before it starts up again, it can be neither increasing nor decreasing its speed. That is to say, a body moving in a horizontal plane will continue in motion at the same velocity, without any further force applied to it, unless it is retarded by an external force in the opposite direction. Therefore, though any change of direction or speed has to be accounted for, the continued forward or upward motion of projectiles requires no explanation. When this horizontal plane becomes a straight line in infinite space, instead of remaining parallel to the Earth's curved surface, Galileo's deduction turns into Newton's law of inertia. The flaws in Aristotle had led to a new system of science.

* For the difficulties in the impetus theory and the hiatus between it and the later theory of inertia, see A. R. Hall, *The Scientific Revolution*, 77-80.

Sir Isaac Newton (1642-1727)

Newton had his predecessors. Not only had Kepler formulated the laws of planetary motion, but Galileo and even Buridan had anticipated the law of inertia. None of this, however, detracts from the dazzling brilliance of Newton's synthesis. Sir Isaac Newton had a mind of the first order, and he fortunately lived at a time when a problem of first magnitude demanded attention. To gain a just respect for his genius, one must at least start to work through hiş theories in some detail; but a popular appreciation has taken the form of Pope's lines, which, far from saying too much, say much too little:

> Nature and Nature's laws lay hid in night;
> God said, Let Newton be! and all was light.

In examining the Newtonian philosophy three points should be kept as distinct as possible. First, there are the concrete scientific details. For example, Book II, Proposition VII, Theorem V:

> If spherical bodies are resisted as the squares of their velocities, in times which are directly as the first motions, and inversely as the first resistances, they will lose parts of their motions proportional to the wholes, and will describe spaces proportional to the product of those times and the first velocities.

Or, again, Proposition XXV, Theorem XX:

> Pendulous bodies that are, in any medium, resisted in the ratio of the moments of time, and pendulous bodies that move in a non-resisting medium of the same specific gravity, perform their

> oscillations in a cycloid in the same time, and describe proportional parts of arcs together.

And, finally, Book III, Proposition XL, Theorem XX:

> That the comets move in some of the conic sections, having their foci in the center of the sun, and by radii drawn to the sun describe areas proportional to the times.

These theorems are then given their full mathematical proof.

There is also a second point to be considered in a study of Newton's work. It is his philosophy of science. What did he think of the nature and purpose of science? Aside from the concrete results embodied in the theorems, how did Newton describe his procedures? What rules of operation did he use? Did he realize he was using them? Or did he claim to proceed in one way when as a matter of fact he was using a different method? One would think that with a little care this second point could be clearly distinguished from the first; and that therefore Newton himself, a most careful mathematician, had no trouble in distinguishing them. Others, at any rate, have become confused; and we would like to avoid such confusion, if possible. To anticipate: Is Newton's law of inertia a scientific detail soundly based on Galileo's observations, or is it an *a priori* philosophic assumption outside the sphere of experiment?

Finally, there is a third point. One wishes to know how Newton influenced his successors. It is commonly said that Newtonian science dominated Western civilization for two full centuries. Many men, both scientists and philosophers, built upon this foundation. How did they build? Were the implications that they drew from Newton's work implications that Newton would have acknowledged? Or, even if some of them are known to contradict certain things that Newton said, are these implications validly drawn nonetheless? Or are they fallacious? And if dominating Western thought means that religion and politics were affected, if a scientific world view is not merely detailed science but a broad philosophy, if morality and art and the values of life are involved, an understanding of these matters also is essential to an educated mind.

Planets and Comets

With respect to the first of these three points–the concrete, scientific details, and how these details soon lead us into broader philosophic inquiries–the easiest approach is planetary motion and, in particular, the theory of comets alluded to in the last of the Newtonian theorems quoted just above.

The study of astronomy, the accurate mathematical description of the daily motions of the stars and the yearly motions of the planets, and even the study of the perplexing comets never died out through the Middle Ages. While not much progress was made with comets, predictions of the positions of the other bodies were remarkably exact. These predictions were made by assuming that the Earth was near the center of the universe and that the planets moved in circular orbits around points which moved in circular orbits around the center of the universe. The Ptolemaic scheme was the theory of epicycles. By means of a single epicycle, for example, the position and the backward and forward motions of Mars could be predicted for a short time; with the addition of other epicycles the apparent motions of Mars could be calculated for a longer period of time; and eventually the Medieval astronomers worked up to forty-some epicycles.

In the first half of the sixteenth century, Copernicus studied Aristarchus and learned that these cumbersome epicycles could be avoided by making the Sun the center or point of reference.

In working out a heliocentric astronomy, Copernicus still retained circular motion, with the result that his predictions were no more accurate and, in fact, less accurate than those of his contemporaries. But the mathematics were simplified and unified. The unification became more evident with Kepler whose three laws, in particular the second and third, applied equations similar in form to all the planets and made the planetary mechanism uniform. Copernicus himself, however, had taken a decisive step, not only in removing the epicycles but also in settling the relative (not absolute) sizes of the planetary spheres, in explaining the fluctuations of the apparent sizes of the heavenly bodies, and in discarding some other small items of Ptolemaic baggage.

Tycho Brahe, a younger Danish astronomer, was not convinced by Copernicus. Both astronomical observation and the reigning philosophy favored geocentrism. For one thing, heliocentric astronomy implies a stellar parallax, and none was discovered. But observation or not, the improvement in the mathematics was indisputable.

At first, Copernicus rested his case merely on the mathematical improvement he had produced. Later he, and not too surprisingly everyone else, fell into the habit of thinking that the planets "really" revolve around the Sun. The scheme became, not merely mathematical, but concretely physical. In this rather natural conclusion were embedded some philosophic questions that agitated many minds for a long time. Other questions will be mentioned later, but at this point the one in which comets played a decisive role will be traced out.

During the late Middle Ages, it was commonly held that the planets were carried around by solid crystalline spheres in which they were embedded. Earlier, the original Ptolemaic astronomy had been the usual view. For Ptolemy, the simple truth was that the planets moved in circles around the Earth. The circles were merely the geometrical paths of the planets. But as Aristotle's writing began to become known, people became persuaded that there must be physical spheres to carry the planets around. The *Tables of London* (A.D. 1232) put the fixed stars in a solid sphere, but not the planets, which moved by themselves in the ether. William of Auvergne (died 1248) had solid spheres, but his views were extremely confused. Less confusion is found in Robert Grosseteste. When he wished to determine the calendar, he used the circles, eccentrics, and epicycles of Ptolemy; but when he philosophized he talked of homocentric spheres. These spheres, however, seem to have come, not from Aristotle, but from a Moslem astronomer, Al Bitrogi. Duns Scotus, a little later (c. 1300), tried to harmonize Ptolemy and Aristotle. Each planet has at least three spheres which surround the Earth. The upper convex surface of the upper sphere and the lower concave surface of the lower sphere are concentric with the Earth. But the lower concave surface of the upper sphere and the upper convex surface of the lower sphere are eccentric to the Earth but concentric with each other. Between these two surfaces is a third sphere, eccentric to the Earth but concentric with the two spheres just described. The three spheres can move without opening an empty space (nature abhors a vacuum), for the thickest part of one sphere is always at the thinnest part of the other. Nor are the spheres fractured, for adjoining surfaces are always concentric.* Tycho Brahe also believed in solid crystalline spheres. Planets, therefore, were thought to move because they were carried around in solid spheres.

These crystalline spheres crumbled under the impact of Copernicus. Heliocentric astronomy obviously could not allow a system of solid spheres to encircle the Earth. But why could not the spheres be reconstructed with the Sun as the center? This would have the advantage of dispensing with Duns Scotus' ingenious expedient. Since Copernicus had the planets rotating

* Compare Pierre Duhem, *Le Système du Monde,* III, 231-498.

in simple circles around the Sun, only one sphere would be needed for each planet. There were, however, other factors at work. In addition to the new astronomy, a new philosophy was taking shape. Strict science, pure mathematics, and observation may not have required the abandonment of spheres; but speculative imagination, jarred loose by the new physical positions of Earth and Sun, took off in a new direction. Reaction against Aristotelian scholasticism had begun. And if Aristotelian geocentrism had now been proved false (though as a matter of fact the proof was still far from complete), then no doubt Aristotle was wrong also in his view that the world is finite in extent. But if the world is infinite, the stars must be scattered through infinite space, and there is no outer sphere.

In this predicament, not only the common mind, but the philosophic mind as well, asked, What, now, makes the planets move?

René Descartes (1596-1650), the founder of modern philosophy, gave an answer to this question. He supposed that matter was divided into extremely small particles. These particles fill all space, for between the larger particles, and all the more between larger visible bodies, there are still smaller particles–so small that they completely fill the interstices without leaving any vacuum. In the heavens, these particles–swirling around in currents and eddies–carry the planets around with them. There are no solid crystalline spheres, but nonetheless the planets are propelled by physical contact.

These Cartesian vortices had the advantage of appealing to familiar experience. Everyone has seen currents and eddies in water and has watched the water carrying twigs and chips in its circular, or possibly elliptical, motion. The theory thus gave a clear answer to the question, What makes the planets move?

Most unfortunately there is one fact of astronomy that ruins Descartes' vortices. It is also incompatible with spheres.

This unpleasant fact is the existence of comets. Comets cut the orbital planes of the planets at all angles and could therefore never be the result of eddies in a celestial fluid. There is also another fact. Planets actually move more slowly as they recede from the Sun, whereas vortices would give the outer planets the greatest velocity. Despite these two conclusive facts, Descartes' vortices competed with Newton's theory of gravitation for many years. Perhaps the widespread hesitation to accept Newton's theory resulted from his answer, or his lack of an answer, to the question, What makes the planets move?

Gravitation

Since the time that Newtonian science won general acceptance, it has been customary to say that a freely falling body falls, and the planets revolve around the Sun, because of gravitation. Now, one of the fatal objections brought against Medieval science was that it appealed to occult qualities. Opium caused sleep, not because of its visible color, not because of its smell or tangible qualities, but because of a hidden soporific or sleep-producing quality. As Newton said,

> The Aristotelians gave the name of occult qualities not to manifest qualities, but to such qualities only as they suppose to lie hid in bodies and to be the unknown causes of manifest effects. . . . Such occult qualities put a stop to the improvement of natural philosophy, and therefore of late years have been rejected. To tell us that every species of things is endowed with an occult specific quality by which it acts and produces manifest effects, is to tell us nothing.

Now Newton's remarks on occult qualities are very much to the point, but they raise the question whether or not gravity is also an occult quality–invisible, intangible, and therefore useless as an explanation of motion. What, then, is gravity?

Cajori, Newton's twentieth-century editor,* collects some of Newton's phrases that seem to make gravity an innate or occult property of matter. These phrases are mostly those in which Newton speaks of one body's attraction for another. Indeed, such an understanding has been quite common. Yet private letters, not published in Newton's lifetime, show that this was not at all his view. For a time, he even entertained the idea of an ether which, by its condensation and rarefaction, would exert pressure on the gravitating bodies. But whether an elastic ether is the proper explanation or not, it was inconceivable to Newton that one body could affect another body without physical contact, unless perchance the motion should be caused by some immaterial spiritual agent.

Newton's final word on the subject was that he did not know what the cause of gravity is. And it was in this context that he made his frequently noted declaration, "*Hypotheses non fingo.*" Or, again in a letter, "Gravity must be caused by an agent acting constantly according to certain laws; but whether this agent be material or immaterial, I have left to the consideration of my readers" (Compare *Principia*, Proposition LXIX, Theorem XXIX, Scholium).

The *General Scholium* at the end of Book III is clear on this point. Since bodies continue in motion, he argues, except as stopped by friction, the planets will continue to move by the mere laws of gravity. "Yet they [the planets] could by no means have at first derived the regular positions of the orbits themselves from those laws." Comets provide conclusive evidence that the solar system could not have arisen through mere mechanical causes. It "could only proceed from the counsel and dominion of an intelligent and powerful Being."

* Florian Cajori, *Newton's Principia,* University of California Press, 1934, Appendix, 632ff.

There then follows some theological exposition, for Newton was convinced that "To discourse of whom [God] from the appearances of things, does certainly belong to natural philosophy." Returning finally to gravitation, he concludes, "But hitherto I have not been able to discover the causes of those properties of gravity from phenomena, and I frame no hypotheses."

Explanation

The preceding material, selected from the history of science, shows clearly enough that the details of scientific fact and law do not exhaust the subject's interest. The history has its importance, to be sure. We want to know that Descartes said this and Newton said that. Even the reasons for rejecting vortices have been given as so much historical information. But not all science is so definitely and narrowly scientific. Philosophic themes also are always interwoven. Therefore, at this point a little reflection on the significance of this historical and scientific advance is called for.

Just above we have read Newton's words, ending with his refusal to explain gravitation. What does this refusal mean? If gravitation cannot be explained, can gravitation explain anything else? What is meant by scientific explanation?

Aside from Newton's remarks on theology, to which we shall return somewhat later, the immediate question is the significance of the law of gravitation for strict science–for the revolution of the planets and for a falling body. Crystalline spheres, Cartesian vortices, and for a time even Newtonian ether were invented to explain what makes the planets move. More particularly, these expedients were invented to explain what makes the planets move in a curved path rather than flying off in a straight line. Not only might Democritus say point-blank that motion does not need to be explained, but indeed, Newton's law of inertia gives the appearance of so saying. However, the law of inertia relates only to rectilinear motion. When a moving body changes the direction of its motion, as the planets constantly do in their elliptical orbits, a cause or explanation is required. That this motivation stands behind the law of gravitation is clearer than any crystalline sphere ever was. Gravity is used chiefly to explain why planets "fall toward" or revolve about the Sun instead of continuing in a straight line according to the first law of motion. But now that the law of gravitation has been worked out with the mathematical precision of inverse squares, do we find explained *quod erat demonstrandum?*

Or the difficulty may be illustrated with a still simpler example. If we ask a person why a stone, when dropped, falls to the ground, and he replies, "Oh, that is because of gravity," has he explained anything at all? Here the difficulty is not found in a change of direction, as is the case with planets, but in two other factors: What makes the stone fall in the first place instead of remaining in mid-air, and what makes it increase its velocity as it falls? Does the law of gravitation answer these questions?

The general law of gravitation is that any two particles attract each other in proportion to the product of their masses and inversely as the square of the distance. When applied to planets and comets, this law turns into Kepler's three laws of planetary motion; when applied to falling stones, it becomes Galileo's law of constant acceleration. The simpler case will be satisfactory for the discussion.

The questions have been asked, Why does a stone fall? What makes it fall? What makes it fall faster? The usual answer is, the law of gravitation. This law as applied to freely falling bodies is that the body falls with an acceleration of thirty-two feet per second per second. Now, to substitute the law itself for its name, the question, Why does a stone fall? is answered by saying that it falls because it falls with an acceleration of thirty-two feet per second per second. But how does a statement of the rate of the fall explain what makes the stone drop in the first place? And how does the rate, ever so carefully measured, explain what makes the stone fall constantly faster? Does it not become clear upon reflection that the law of gravitation is not an explanation? It explains neither the fall of the stone nor the revolution of the planets.

Here we begin to see how the details of science and the principles of philosophy become intertwined and even confused. Galileo and Newton by their great genius worked out their respective laws in strict mathematical form. This was science. Let no one underestimate its importance! Of course not; we resolve never to underestimate the importance of science–if only we can find out what that importance is. We have arrived at the scientific law of gravitation, or, at least, Newton arrived there for us; but now we are asking, and even Newton himself began to ask, about its significance. This is not science; it is philosophy. Let no one underestimate the importance of philosophy!

The philosophy of science, in distinction from science itself as ordinarily understood, must consider the significance of scientific law. Does science explain anything? Must we not go beyond science, and if we do not care for occult qualities, must we not, like Newton, explain the origin (at least) of the solar system as the result of a Supreme Intelligence? Must we not proceed from physics to metaphysics? Surely we want to know more than the path of the planets and the acceleration of a freely falling body. Facts such as these are interesting and important. But a statement of fact is not an explanation: It is the very thing that needs to be explained. Viewed in this light, science explains nothing.

Well, then, this light, some scientists contend, must be

the wrong light. The true light, they say, is that science explains. Since, obviously, science does not explain what makes a stone fall, these men conclude that the wrong question has been asked. Explanation must be defined by what science can do; what science cannot do is not to be called explanation. Any question science cannot answer–whether it have the semblance of science like the cause of a body's fall, or whether *a fortiori* it be an ultimate metaphysical question such as the existence of God–is not a proper question. One should not ask these questions. One should ask only questions science can answer. And there is such a question. Science may not be able to explain what makes a body fall, but it can answer–and can answer with amazing mathematical precision–*how* a body falls: with an acceleration of thirty-two feet per second per second. Science answers *how.* Any other question is nonsense. Explanation is description.

As Morris R. Cohen put it,

> A sharp distinction is often drawn between description and explanation, but a scientific explanation is after all only a certain kind of description, a description in which the phenomenon is related to other phenomena in accordance with certain laws. Thus we explain the rainbow by calling attention to the law of refraction of light. . . . Note that the law of refraction is not something antecedent in time to the occurrence of rainbows. The rainbow is only one of the ways or occurrences of refraction. . . . A law is not a force which compels its instances to conform to it. Thus the law of gravitation is a description in mathematical terms of the spatio-temporal relations of all bodies, celestial as well as terrestrial. . . . That it was possible to formulate the law in the way Newton did was due to the empirical

> fact that observations on the moon and on falling bodies fit in with this formula. This in no way answers to the popular notion of a cause as a force which compels objects to behave in a certain way rather than in another.*

Of course, this view of explanation, and in particular this view of science, was not Newton's view. Planets and stones in motion without anything having set them in motion were inconceivable to him. The law of gravitation could not have put the planets in their orbits. Without the operation of a Supreme Intelligence, the solar system cannot be explained. But if Newton was right on these points, then *how* is not the only question that can legitimately be asked; experimental science is not the only path to truth; and a philosophy of science is needed to determine its range of application and its limitations. The necessity of non-scientific or non-experimental principles becomes all the clearer when we examine this view of explanation itself. The confident claim that *how* is the only legitimate question is not an experimental laboratory discovery. Nor is it itself a description of any physical motions. On what ground, then, can such a statement be made? How does one recognize that God is not the true light and that something else is? Once again it is clear that scientists, wittingly or unwittingly, make and must make use of a philosophy.

Mechanistic Philosophy

Science, the history of science, and the philosophy of science are, as we have seen, so inextricably fused or confused that it is impossible to draw definite boundaries between them. Yet some people believe that the boundaries are most distinct

* *The Meaning of Human History,* Open Court, 1947, 99.

and obvious. Therefore, at times scientists accuse philosophers of being unscientific and ignoring the facts. Science deals in facts! Philosophers reply by convicting scientists of accepting as facts the philosophic assumptions that underlie their laws. Or, what is worse, they charge scientists with being unaware that they use philosophic assumptions. Scientists frequently think that their results spring directly and solely from experimentation quite apart from philosophic speculation and ethereal metaphysics. Difficulties such as these increase with the development of Newtonian science into mechanistic philosophy.

Mechanism was the dominant scientific worldview of the nineteenth century. It was regarded as the most comprehensive and final conclusion of scientific investigation. Even in this, the second half of the twentieth century, mechanism is not without defenders. But since it now also faces opposition from the scientists themselves, one must determine whether it is really science or merely a superstitious metaphysics; and if the latter, one must decide how to replace it with a sound philosophy or perchance to do without philosophy and metaphysics altogether. Hence, the immediate aim is to show how the modern methods of science led to mechanism, what mechanism is, and eventually to indicate the effect on this philosophy of the twentieth-century revolution in science.

To examine the relation between science and mechanism, something beyond straight history must first be given concerning the scientific method. Scientific method, as has been said, is held in great repute today. College courses in sociology, development of civilization (where a student learns all about everything in one semester), and even English never tire of singing its praises. But when a student of physics, who has been using the scientific method in his laboratory experiments, later reads divergent accounts of it, he–if not the sociology and other majors–understands the difficulty of defining it precisely. Yet until defined, its relationship to mechanism remains in doubt.

Now, however difficult it may be to formulate an exact account of the scientific method, it is relatively easy to mention some differences between the Aristotelian procedure, now branded as unscientific, and the modern methods.

Contrary to popular impressions, the difference between Aristotelian and modern science is not that the former is deductive and the latter empirical. Galileo and every modern scientist has formulated hypotheses and then deduced their consequences. Without such deduction, modern science could not proceed. Nor is the difference that modern science is observational and empirical, and Aristotelian procedure is not. Aristotle and many other ancients were excellent observers. Though he failed to discover the speed of light, Aristotle observed that heavy bodies fall faster than lighter ones and accounted for it by differing resistance to a medium.

Perhaps the main difference–the source of other differences–is that modern scientists experiment on principle, whereas the ancients only observed, or at most experimented on a very small scale without any definite plan. Today's scientist does not sit and wait for some natural event to happen by chance. He deliberately does something. Galileo, for example, although his study of the pendulum may have started accidentally, did not wait to observe some chance body fall from whatever height it happened to be. Contrary to the popular story, he did not even drop weights from the leaning tower of Pisa. He deliberately rolled marbles down an inclined trough which he had carefully smoothed and polished. Such planned experimentation is the factor by which John Dewey liked most of all to commend the modern method. The experimenter does things to the material he is examining. He cuts it, or heats it, or dissolves it in acid, or passes an electric current through it, or what not.

This systematic experimentation logically requires, and historically developed, a technique. Not only did Galileo prepare his trough and roll the marbles down, but what is more, he varied the length of their descent. This means he measured the distances; he measured the times also. And he made these measurements for the purpose of manipulating them mathematically. One of his mathematical analyses showed that varying the velocity with the distance presupposes infinite speed; and since this is impossible, he assumed that the velocity increases with the time. From this assumption, this law, this mathematical equation, it can be deduced that a body falls four times as far in two seconds as in one. Later scientists used more mathematics; indeed, they invented more mathematics to use. Today everyone who watches astronauts on television has seen blackboards full of cryptic formulas. In ancient physics, mathematics was largely unused; but mathematics is the soul, or should one materialistically say the "mainspring," of modern science. Kepler expressed the idea nicely, saying that as the ears were made for sound and the eyes for color, so the mind of man is meant to measure quantity, and it wanders in darkness when it leaves the realm of quantitative thought.*

The use of mathematics highlights another important difference between ancient and modern science. After Galileo had mathematically deduced from his first formula the consequence that a body falls four times as far in two seconds as in one, he measured his rolling marbles again to see if they actually did so. That is to say, the mathematical deduction is a prediction that may be verified by a later experiment. Prediction and verification are of the essence of modern scientific method. Of course, ancient astronomy made brilliant use of mathematics, at least geometry. Predictions also were essential, and the predictions were tested by later observation. But these anticipations of modern methods were largely confined to astronomy. Physics, not to mention chemistry, was quite another thing.

* Butterfield, *The Origin of Modern Science,* 67.

The rapid advances of the new scientific method–not only on the grand celestial scale of Kepler and Newton, but as well in the innumerable details of the pendulum and small machines, atmospheric pressure, physical optics, thermodynamics, the atomic theory, etc.–confirmed the limitless power of mathematics and the fruitfulness of quantitative measurement. Therefore, the thesis was inevitable that all natural phenomena are amenable to this method. As Laplace put it: Give me the positions and velocities of every particle in the universe and I can calculate their positions at any future time. This thesis is the thesis of mechanism. The universe is viewed as a machine and the predictions of the mathematical formulas are actualized of necessity. Nothing contrary to the mathematics could possibly occur.*

That the astronomical heavens are mechanical was not a new idea. It is no more Copernican than Ptolemaic. Descartes with his vortices and Newton's theory of gravitation were not too startling so far as the idea of mechanical motion is concerned. But what was startling, disturbing, and controversial was the extension of the mechanical ideal to all phenomena, including life, and especially human life.

Descartes had been willing enough to regard animals as unconscious machines. Punch the right button and a yelp comes

* The definition of mechanics given by Laplace, though expressed most simply, can hardly be improved upon. Contemporary discussions now try to be more technical or at least more pedantic. The phrase "process law" has come into use, and mechanism is defined as the theory that all scientific explanation takes the form of process laws. But, in the first place, the term *process* law is less widely understood than the term *mathematical* law. And, second, even Gustav Bergmann, who prefers the word *process,* admits that "even when we know processes, as we do in physics, the law is not actually stated in this form, but, as I mentioned before, as a system of differential equations" *(Philosophy of Science,* 93). Hence, it seems satisfactory to define mechanism as the theory that holds that the universe consists of particles whose motions can be described and whose future positions can, therefore, be predicted by differential equations. Conversely, mechanism is denied when the least particles are said to be unpredictable individually; in which case, their behavior is describable only by statistical laws.

out. But Descartes knew that he himself was not just a machine; he was a thinking being–*Cogito ergo sum.* Thinking is something that machines cannot do; and by this thinking, including willing, Descartes was able to alter, if not the constant quantity of motion in the universe, at least the direction of the motions around the pineal gland and so control his own conduct. However, despite this intimate experience of thinking, a nonmechanical man in a mechanical universe results in an awkward dualism. Spinoza, with his strong tendency toward unity, would not have man as a kingdom within a kingdom. The laws of nature could permit of no exception. Mechanical law must be inviolable. Even Locke in a skeptical moment said that for all he knew a body might be able to think. In which case a soul would be unnecessary. Then the French writer, La Mettrie (1709-1751), abolished spiritual principles in his book *L'Homme Machine.*

> L'âme n'est donc qu'un vain terme dont on n'a point d'idée, et dont un bon esprit ne doit se servir que pour nommer la partie qui pense en nous. Posé le moindre principe de mouvement, les corps animés auront tout ce qu'il leur faut pour se mouvoir, sentir, penser, se repentir, et se conduire en un mot dans le Physique et dans le Moral qui en depend. [But], C'est une folie de perdre le temps à en rechercher le méchanisme. La nature du mouvement nous est aussi inconnue que celle de la matière. . . . Qu'on m'accorde seulement que la matière organisée est douée d'un principe moteur . . . c'en est assez . . . [Aram Vartanian, ed., Princeton University Press, 1960, 180, 189].

The scientific details of La Mettrie are not superior to the level of the eighteenth century; some of his arguments seem superficial today; they should not be judged by present standards. A more thoroughgoing attempt to reduce life to physicochemical law is to be found in *The Mechanistic Conception of Life* (1912) by Jacques Loeb.

Now, if the body needs no soul, as La Mettrie argued, it was easy for another Frenchman, Baron d'Holbach (1723-1789), to conclude that the universe needs no God. As with Spinoza, the universe is purposeless and, consequently, theism is a disease caused by some derangement of man's mechanism.

Cabanis (1757-1808) then attempted to formulate a materialistic and mechanistic psychology. He itemized the influence of age, sex, health, climate, *etc.*, on the so-called mind. It was he who invented the too convenient phrase, "The brain secretes thought as the liver secretes bile." Nevertheless, he tried to avoid metaphysics by refusing to discuss "primary causes"; and the excellent historian of French philosophy, Lévy-Bruhl, contends that for this reason he should not be called a materialist.

In Germany during the nineteenth century, materialism found leadership in the work of Moleschott, Büchner, and Vogt. Force and matter were the ultimate realities. The principle of the conservation of matter was one foundation of this materialism, and the corresponding principle of the conservation of energy was used to support the ideas of mechanism and determinism. The wide acceptance of this point of view–the materialism, the atheism, and the naive arrogance of absolute certainty–can be judged by the fact that Ludwig Büchner's *Kraft und Stoff* passed through at least seventeen German and twenty-two foreign editions. Prefacing his first chapter with the slogan, "Where there are three students of nature, there are two atheists," he opens the body of his text with eleven assertions of materialism by as many different authors. Beyond these, it will be interesting and instructive to sample his own vigorous assertions.

> Those who talk about an independent or supernatural creative force, which has evolved the universe out of itself or out of nothing, are in

antagonism with the first and simplest axiom of a philosophical view of nature [*Force and Matter,* English ed., 1891, 8].

Matter as such is indestructible. . . . "A simple elemental atom," says B. Stewart, "is really an immortal being." . . . Matter must have been eternal . . . the universe must be untreated . . . today the indestructibility or permanence of matter is a scientific fact firmly established [14-19].

Motion is a necessary and indispensable attribute of matter. . . . Physical astronomy teaches us with absolute certainty. . . . It follows hence with absolute certainty that motion is as eternal and uncreatable . . . as force or matter. . . . According to Holbach *(Système de la Nature)* the world is nothing more than matter and motion. . . . Matter and motion are eternal. . . . And all this is entirely borne out by modern science [58-66].

Natural laws are immutable. . . . The experience of more than a thousand years has pressed on observers the conviction of the immutability of natural laws . . . with such absolute certainty, that not the least doubt can remain. . . . With the most absolute truth and with the greatest scientific certainty can we say at this day: There is nothing miraculous in the world. . . . The ghost of a personal, universal spirit, interfering in natural processes, has long been banished from astronomy, physics, and chemistry. . . . The ignorant layman may believe in a personal god; but the scientist or the educated layman . . . would place his reason below that of the simplest peasant, if he believed in such a one without foundation. . . . Belief

> in God is therefore almost confined at the present time to those so-called learned men who know scarcely anything about natural processes. . . . Whatever theological interest or narrow-minded pedantry can urge in opposition to this, is controverted by the strength of the facts, which in this respect leave no room for any doubt [75-81].
>
> Thinking can and must be regarded as a special mode of general natural motion, which is as characteristic of the substance of the central nervous elements as the motion of contraction is of the muscle-substance, or the motion of light is of the universal ether. . . . The words *mind, spirit, thought, sensibility, volition, life,* designate no entities and no things real, but only properties, capacities, actions, of the living substance, or results of entities, which are based upon material form of existence [242-243].

It is the judgment of Dampier-Whettham (*A History of Science,* 445) that "At the beginning of the twentieth century the majority of men of science held unconsciously a naive materialism, or, if they thought at all about such problems, inclined to the phenomenalism of Mach and Karl Pearson, or the evolutionary monism of Haeckel or of W. K. Clifford."

Among science-philosophers of the twentieth century there has been a tendency, not only to disclaim materialism for themselves, but also to minimize its extent and importance in the nineteenth century. This interpretation of the history of scientific philosophy is supported in two ways. The first is the cautious skepticism of some writers. For example, we have just seen how Lévy-Bruhl hesitated to call Cabanis a materialist because of his ostensible avoidance of ultimate questions. Even La Mettrie is not a second Hobbes. F. H. Lange (1828-1875), in his famous *History of Materialism,* is a more convincing example. Lange was a sort of Kantian with an unknowable reality; since it is unknowable we cannot affirm that it is either material or mental, with the result that, although the *a priori* categories force us to think mechanistically, metaphysical materialism is skeptically avoided.

Another device for escaping the distasteful label of materialism is to insist that by strict definition materialism is the theory of hard little pellets moving in empty space. Thus if a writer denies empty space and assumes a continuous elastic or ethereal body, he cannot be called a materialist. Perhaps he might be called a corporealist, and if he imitates Spinoza and attributes sensation to body, we might call him a hylozoist.

This is the position of Ernst Haeckel in *The Riddle of the Universe.* Although his preface modestly disclaims omniscience, he is very sure that the conservation of matter and the conservation of energy are the two supreme laws of nature. Their discovery is the greatest intellectual triumph of the nineteenth century. In consecutive sentences he says,

> The premature death of Spinoza, Raphael, Schubert, and many other great men . . . is . . . enough . . . to destroy the untenable myth of a "wise Providence" and of an "All-loving Father in heaven." The existence of ether (or cosmic ether) as a real element is a *positive fact* [italics his] and has been known as such for the last twelve years [*The Riddle of the Universe,* Harper & Brothers, 1901, 225].

His interest in ether and the conservation of matter is equalled and perhaps excelled by his antipathy to Christianity, not only in the form of Romish corruption and intrigue but in the form of liberal Protestantism as well. The belief in creation, providence, and miracles is incompatible with the law of the persistence of matter and force (235). Even the liberal Protestant ministers entertain ideas of God that are directly opposed to all scientific experience (10). Science has already "amply demonstrated" (13) that the universe is eternal, that substance has two attributes–matter and energy– and that organic life has resulted from the water that was produced by the geological cooling of the Earth.

Haeckel avoids ordinary materialism by his Spinozism. Matter cannot exist without spirit, nor spirit without matter. "Matter, or infinitely extended substance, and spirit (or energy) or sensitive and thinking substance are the two fundamental attributes . . . of the all embracing divine essence of the world, the universal substance" (20-21). Therefore he can also say, "Consciousness, thought, and speculation are functions of the ganglionic cells of the cortex of the brain."

Such scientific dogmatism may not be atomic materialism. Spinoza similarly tried to avoid the charge of atheism by calling nature God. Since, however, he denied the existence of a personal, transcendent creator of the universe, it is merely a play on words to insist that he was not an atheist. So too, when thought is identified as a secretion or as the motions of the ganglionic cells, it is but a play on words to claim that materialism has been abandoned. However, let anyone who wishes insist on the quibble: The type of science here under discussion is mechanism. It is a method which depends on quantitative measurement and disregards qualities. Its results are differential equations, and its philosophy is that nothing exists that can violate mechanical law.

No doubt, differential equations have their own aesthetic appeal; but can this appeal occur in a world completely quantitative, devoid of qualities? It has already been explained that the Medieval scientists affirmed, and that Newton denied, the value of occult qualities. These alleged qualities suffered from a twofold defect: They could not be observed, and even when assumed they were useless for purposes of explanation. But the ordinary type of quality also–however easily observable–proved to be, in the eyes of Galileo and Newton, equally useless for scientific purposes. In studying the pendulum or the lever, no one thinks of paying attention to its color. Whether the pendulum is red or blue makes not the least difference. Similarly, if one studies the effects of acids on metals, the taste is unimportant. And if one drops a ball to see the angle of its bounce, the sound it makes as it strikes the surface has nothing to do with the aim of the experiment. These so-called secondary qualities may therefore be ignored.

Not only because they are useless may they be ignored; a little reflection will show that red and blue, sweet and sour, loud and soft, hot and cold do not really exist. Galileo considered the phenomenon of heat. The ordinary opinion, in his day and today, was that heat is a real quality actually residing in the thing that we say is hot. But as Galileo thought over the constitution of body or matter, he came to the conclusion that matter in its own nature is possessed of size and shape; in relation to other bodies, a piece of matter may be large or small; it may move or remain at rest; it touches or it does not touch another body. These characteristics are absolutely inseparable from body; we cannot detach them physically, nor can we even think them detached. The status of the secondary qualities, however, is quite otherwise. If we were beings of pure reason and did not possess senses, we probably would have never had any idea of such qualities. Instead of being actually in the bodies, red and sweet and hot are merely reactions that occur in the mind of a sensitive organism. Were sensation abolished, red and hot would no longer appear anywhere.

A striking illustration of this viewpoint is Galileo's experiment with a feather. Suppose a feather moves, it has a size and shape, and we touch it. But if it is brushed on the upper lip just under the nostrils, it tickles. Brush it on the back of the fingers, it does not tickle. Now, says Galileo, this tickling is all in us, and not in the feather, and if the animate and sensitive body be removed (and the feather be brushed over a marble statue) the tickling no longer exists. The same is true for tastes, colors, odors, and sounds.

Newton also denied the real existence of secondary qualities. Speaking of color, he said that the rays of light are not strictly colored. In them there is nothing else than a certain power to stir up a sensation in the mind. Similarly, sound in a bell is nothing but a trembling motion, and sound in the air is nothing but the consequent motion of the air. Color and sound, therefore, exist only in the mind of the person who senses them. And if the mind is precisely the motion of the ganglionic cells, then colors and sounds are precisely motions inside our skulls. Would it complicate the argument too much if we also ask this question here: If the red that we see is not a quality of the body we see, but is only a motion in the brain, then are not the bodies we see and the motions we describe in those differential equations also merely the motions of the brain?

The rejection of secondary qualities is the negative side of the scientific viewpoint; the positive side is that quantity is real. Insistence on quantitative measurement–or, better, this restriction of science to mathematical relationships among points in space–was in decided contrast to the Medieval and Aristotelian procedure. In Scholastic philosophy, one of the important scientific concepts was that of qualitative change. Experience presents innumerable examples: birth, growth, and death; the changes of the weather; the spoilage of food; the melting of ice; and the boiling of water. All these are instances of qualitative change. But when secondary qualities are considered unreal and when spatial measurement displaces all other sensory observation, then qualitative change no longer holds any interest for science. If there are no qualities, there can be no qualitative change.

This new scientific outlook soon produced an interesting and important result. In the Aristotelian view some bodies were heavy and other bodies were light. That is, qualitative differences were the basis of two quite different species of body–so different that the same laws could not apply to both. Earth and water were heavy, and they naturally fell toward the center of the Earth; air and fire were light, and their natural motion was upward toward the heavens. But with the new mathematical method of measuring space, experiments were soon devised to show that air had weight. Two brass hemispheres were placed together and the air inside was exhausted. The external air pressure then made it almost impossible to pull the hemispheres apart. Again, a tube of mercury, that is, a barometer, was carried up a mountain, and the height of the column was observed to decrease as the altitude increased. These results are interesting enough in themselves, but more important is the generalization based on them–namely, that all bodies are alike and that one type of law will cover all nature.

Instead, therefore, of nature's being composed of heavy, light, hot, cold, and colored bodies subject to qualitative change, nature is composed of hard, impenetrable, tiny pellets or atoms which move in space but which do not change in themselves. Newton put it this way: "God in the beginning formed matter in solid, massy, hard, impenetrable, moveable particles . . . incomparably harder than any porous bodies compounded of them." Essentially this is the view of Aristotle's ancient rival, Democritus. Atomism is the theory that the world is composed of small particles moving in empty space. All observed phenomena result from the rearrangement of the atoms. The phenomena of life and mind, likewise, are to be explained by more complicated arrangements and motions.

Of course, Newton himself did not intend to deny the existence of God and the soul; but the implications of his theory were understood as doing so. A contemporary author asserts,

> Newton's authority was squarely behind that view of the cosmos which saw in man a puny irrelevant spectator (so far as a being wholly

> imprisoned in a dark room can be called such) of the vast mathematical system whose regular motions according to mechanical principles constituted the world of nature. The gloriously romantic world of Dante . . . the world that people had thought themselves living in–a world rich with colour and sound, redolent with fragrance, filled with gladness, love and beauty . . . was crowded now into minute corners in the brains of scattered organic beings. The really important world outside was a world hard, cold, colourless, silent and dead [E. A. Burtt, *The Metaphysical Foundations of Modern Science,* 236].

It is even a matter of dispute whether the real world–the atoms–can be hard, for hard seems to be a quality too, rather than a geometrical dimension. But it is indisputably "a world of quantity, a world of mathematically computable motions in mechanical regularity" in which human aspirations can be but mysterious chemical effects in complicated carbon compounds.

Bertrand Russell has written a much quoted paragraph to the effect that man is the product of causes which had no prevision of his emergence; that his hopes and fears are the accidental collocations of atoms; that no heroism or intensity of thought can preserve an individual life beyond the grave; that all human labor, inspiration, and genius are destined to extinction and will be buried beneath the debris of a universe in ruins. And with finality he says, "All these things, if not quite beyond dispute, are yet so nearly certain, that no philosophy which rejects them can hope to stand" *(Mysticism and Logic,* 47,56).

It is now obvious that science has arrived at conclusions of religious, ethical, and human import. But is it still science? Is it not rather scientism? Has not the dim boundary between science and philosophy been somewhere crossed? It must have been; for although the denial of miracles may seem scientific because of the incompatibility of miracles and mathematical law, the existence of God and the immortality of the soul and the value of human life as opposed to despair are matters of theology and ethics rather than of mathematical physics. Even the conservation of matter and the existence of ether–so amply demonstrated twelve years before Haeckel's *Riddle*–may be philosophy, bad philosophy, rather than good science.

Absolute and Final Truth

But many of the scientists and most of the leaders of public opinion took all this as absolute and final truth. Karl Pearson, for example, in his famous *Grammar of Science* taught, "The classification of facts and the formation of absolute judgments upon the basis of this classification–judgments independent of the idiosyncracies of the individual mind–essentially sum up *the aim and method of modern science.*" That the absolute judgments of science extend to theology and ethics, Pearson asserts in the following:

> The goal of science is clear–it is nothing short of the complete interpretation of the universe. . . . Science does much more than demand that it shall be left in undisturbed possession of what the theologian and metaphysician please to call its "legitimate field." It claims that the whole range of phenomena, mental as well as physical–the entire universe–is its field. It asserts that the scientific method is the sole gateway to the whole region of knowledge [6, 14, 24].

W. K. Clifford also extends science into ethics when he says, "It is wrong always, everywhere, and for anyone, to believe anything upon insufficient evidence."

This implies that, with perhaps the exception of some minor lapses in morality, Clifford himself had sufficient evidence for his scientific and anti-theological principles.

Professor A. J. Carlson made a particularly vigorous statement of this viewpoint. Although his professional work was not in the exact sciences, for which reason one might have expected him to be less dogmatic than a physicist, his expressions are quite intransigent and have been unusually influential because of having been twice published *(Science,* 73:217-225, 1931; and *The Scientific Monthly,* 59:85-95, 1944). The article "Science and the Supernatural," states,

> What is the method of science? In essence it is this–the rejection *in toto* of all non-observational and non-experimental authority in the field of experience. . . . When no evidence is produced [in favor of a pronouncement] other than personal dicta, past and present "revelations" in dreams, or the "voice of God," the scientist can pay no attention whatsoever, except to ask, How do they get that way?

Carlson then confidently asserts, "The scientist tries to rid himself of all faiths and beliefs. He either knows or he does not know. If he knows, there is no room for faith or belief. If he does not know, he has no right to faith or belief."

This attitude of absolutism is more characteristic of the nineteenth century than of the twentieth, and it is interesting to note this extreme of dogmatism just at the time when the Newtonian foundation was being swept away. Indeed, to one's surprise, it is found in twentieth-century writers, other than Carlson, who ought to have known better.

Hans Reichenbach *(Modern Philosophy of Science,* 136, 149) contrasts the perennial inability of philosophers to agree on anything with the common ground, universally recognized, which science has developed. A science teacher can teach "with the proud feeling of introducing his students into a realm of well-established truth." The results of science are "established with a superpersonal validity and universally accepted."

Now, Reichenbach does not oppose all systems of philosophy. The philosophy of analysis, which refrains from indulging in independent construction, is commendable. Other philosophies are individualistic and glamorous creations of art, but the philosophy of analysis enjoys "the advantage of paving the path to universal agreement, of setting up results that eventually will be exempt from controversy and attack. It is the path of science on which the philosophy of logical analysis is marching. Though less attractive to the romantic mind, the adoption of the scientific method will appear the inescapable consequence of an unprejudiced study of the history of philosophy."

Ernest Nagel also has inherited a tinge of dogmatism. In his presidential address of 1954, he recognizes that scientists and science-philosophers became acutely skeptical in the second quarter of the present century. This led to a narrow specialization that is not to be wholly deplored. Nevertheless, Nagel insists, scientific thinkers hold, sometimes subconsciously, certain comprehensive assumptions concerning the overall nature of things. Now, a philosopher owes it to himself to articulate his basic assumptions, and, concludes Nagel, the findings of the various positive sciences support some and disconfirm others of these broad generalizations. Specifically, naturalism is a sound generalized account of the world, repeatedly confirmed by centuries of human experience. The causal primacy of organized matter, the contingency of events on the organization of spatio-temporally located bodies, is one of the best-tested conclusions of experience. There is no place for an immaterial spirit or for the survival of personality after the body decays. These principles, he repeats, are supported by compelling evidence, conclusive evidence.

Thus it is clear that if Nagel is not so brash as Clifford and Carlson, he is very confident that science supports naturalism. This tremendous pride in the permanent truth of the generalized scientific formulas has often been used also by liberal theologians in their attack on orthodox believers. Rudolf Bultmann, competing with Karl Barth for first place in the present theological lineup, retains the nineteenth-century absolutism even more than Nagel or Reichenbach. In *Kerygma and Myth* he combines a confidence in the permanence of scientific law with a rejection of the belief in spirits: "Now that the forces and laws of nature have [really] been discovered, we can no longer believe in spirits, whether good or evil" (4). Consistently, he should deny the existence of God, for God is a good spirit; but he seems to be not quite that consistent. And then in *Jesus Christ and Mythology* (36-38) he borrows from Auguste Comte and asserts that although science may change in some details, the method of thinking will never change again. He goes even further and seems to suggest that whereas geocentric and heliocentric astronomy may continue to change, the (Newtonian?) laws of motion are immutable truths.

Contrasting sharply with Bultmann and scientific dogmatism in general, the statement of Philipp Frank *(Philosophy of Science,* 90) is a modest anticipation of what follows: "It took a long time for the present-day theory of motion to develop, and we do not know whether or not it is the right scheme for the future."

Criticism

It is well known that the scientific developments of the twentieth century have greatly altered the Newtonian worldview. Hence, before continuing with the more recent history, we must pause here to summarize and evaluate the older position. The Newtonian laws of motion had given rise to a philosophy of mechanism. All events occurred by means of collisions among atoms. Nothing inconsistent with the mathematical equations could take place. These laws were fixed, absolute, accurate descriptions of how nature works. Therefore, there could be no miracles, no soul, no personal immortality, no God; and life in the dead, dark universe was to be lived on a basis of unyielding despair.

The purpose of this next section of argument is to show that Newtonian science, quite apart from any twentieth-century reversal, cannot validly support these conclusions. The picture of science is itself mistaken, and its extension to religious affairs is unwarranted.

First of all, the processes of science as actually carried on in the laboratories do not justify the conclusion that the laws of mechanics describe how nature works. Newtonian laws never were discoveries pure and simple. Contrary to Carlson, these laws do not exclude all non-observational and non-experimental authority. At best, scientific law is a construction rather than a discovery; and the construction depends on factors never seen under a microscope, never weighed in a balance, never handled or manipulated.

To justify these criticisms, the law of the pendulum will serve as an adequate example. The law of the pendulum states that the period of the swing is proportional to the square root of the length. If, however, the weight of the bob is unevenly displaced around its center, the law will not hold. The law assumes that the bob is homogeneous, that the weight is symmetrically distributed along all axes, or (more technically) that the mass is concentrated at a point. No such bob exists, and hence the law is not an accurate description of any tangible pendulum. Second, the law assumes that the pendulum swings by a tensionless string. There is no such string, so the scientific law does not describe any physical pendulum. And third, the law could be true only if the pendulum swung on an axis without friction. There is no such axis. It follows, therefore, that no visible pendulum accords with the mathematical formula, and that the formula is not a description of any physical pendulum.

It is to be noted that this example does not depend upon the distinction between grandfather's clocks too tall for the shelf and pendulums under laboratory conditions. The most carefully constructed laboratory pendulum still falls short of the ideal requirements. Only an ideal pendulum, only an imaginary pendulum, only a non-existing pendulum is described by the Newtonian law.

Therefore, since the Newtonian laws do not describe the actual workings of nature, they cannot be used as a satisfactory demonstration of the impossibility of God and miracles. If this conclusion seems a little premature, it will be necessary to show more completely that non-observational factors are essential ingredients in scientific law.

To do this, we must more carefully examine the process of experimentation. No matter how intricate an experiment may be, its basic process is the measurement of a line. If a scientist is attempting to determine the boiling point of a fluid, he measures the length of the mercury in a thermometer. If he is interested in the specific gravity of this or that, he measures the distance between a zero mark on a balance and another mark on the scale. Whatever the experiment may be, all measurement is the measurement of the length of a line.

When this length has been measured once, the scientist in any new and important experiment repeats the experiment and measures the length a second, a third, a fourth time, until he has a long list of readings. These measurements are the experimental factors; these are the observational data; but they are not the sole factors in arriving at laws. After the scientist has obtained his list of readings, he notices that they are all different. Water never, well, hardly ever, boils at the same temperature. A cubic centimeter of gold hardly ever weighs the same twice. Thus a list of different readings is an inescapable result of measuring.

With this list of readings, the scientist does what seems to be only sound common sense. He adds them and divides by the number of readings; that is, he computes the arithmetic mean. For philosophical purposes this step should be carefully considered. Why is it sound common sense to compute the arithmetic mean? For many people, it seems the natural thing to do because they have a notion that we need an average, and the arithmetic mean is the only average they know. But statisticians know two other averages: the mode–or the most frequently occurring number–and the median–or the middle number in the list when arranged in order of magnitude. Why then does the scientist choose the mean rather than one of the other two? This question turns out to be more difficult to answer than at first it might seem; but whatever answer is attempted, clearly nothing in the observational data has dictated its choice. Here is something the scientist himself contributes, no doubt from his theory of mathematics. It is certainly neither imposed upon him by, nor discovered by him in, the experimental material.*

This is only the beginning of the use of non-empirical factors in the construction of a law of physics. The next step is the scientist's subtraction of each reading from the mean to find the difference. One reading may be .002 above the mean and another .003 below. When these differences are ascertained, the scientist–disregarding the plus or minus signs–adds them and divides by the number of readings, thus computing the arithmetic mean of the differences. This mean he attaches with a plus and minus sign to the original mean (for example, 19.31 ± .0025) and calls it the variable error. Once more the procedure is

* The physicist uses other averages also. The geometric mean, used in double weighing, seems less arbitrary; but in reality it depends on the theory of the lever, which itself has been obtained in the manner described. There is also a harmonic average, and a standard deviation. The latter includes a squared number, squared because of the theory of least squares. But one might have cubed the number and attached it to a theory of least cubes.

dictated by something other than the observed data.

After the scientist has done this for a whole series of experiments–for example, the boiling point of a liquid at many pressures, or the force of gravity between the same two bodies at many distances–his next step is a most striking confirmation of the conclusion that a law of physics is a construction and not a discovery of how nature moves. The step from the several means with their variable errors to the equation that will be called the law may be made by plotting these values on a graph. But, of course, instead of indicating a point on the graph, the value 19.31 ± .0025 indicates a line; the corresponding range of pressure or force indicates another line on the other axis, with the result that the two values enclose a rectangular area on the graph. The scientist marks out a series of such areas, each one corresponding to one of the experiments in the whole set.

Then he passes a curve through these areas, and this curve he calls a law. But here is the trouble. Through one series of rectangles it is possible to pass any number of curves. Even through a series of points apparently on a straight line it is equally easy to pass a straight line or a sine curve. In fact, it is to be particularly noted that through a series of areas an infinite number of different curves may be passed. The empirical data do not necessitate any given curve. In other words, so far as observation is concerned, the scientist could have chosen a law other than the one he actually selected. Indeed, his range of selection was infinite; and out of this infinity he chose, he did not discover, the equation he accepts.

Not only does this consideration show that laws are not discovered in the empirical material, or necessarily deduced from that material, but it also shows that if mathematical equations could describe nature, the chance of choosing the correct description is one over infinity, or zero. Therefore, all the laws of physics are false.

Quae cum ita sint as our old high school Latin friends would say, it follows that the philosophy of mechanism is not an empirical conclusion so fixed and absolute that some other belief would be immoral. It is not sufficient to rule out either miracles in this world or immortality in the next. Nor is it something "so nearly certain" that we must exchange faith in God for despair, whether yielding or unyielding. Mechanism may for this or that reason seem to be plausible in the eyes of some philosophers, but it is not a scientific necessity.

The true state of affairs can be disclosed more fully by another consideration. The question is, How does one arrive at the view that the universe is a mechanism? It is certainly not a valid deduction from experience. Rather, it is a leap of faith. All of us, scientists included, have ordinary experience of living beings, animals and men; we also have ordinary experience of machines. The differences between the two sorts of things are obvious. Now, shall we jump to the conclusion that man and the universe as a whole are machines, or shall we jump to the conclusion that freely falling bodies and the universe as a whole are living beings? Many of the ancients pictured the universe as a living being. Such a view is not an unknown oddity, however much it may seem so to recent materialists. Not only some ancients, but some modern philosophers also held that the universe is alive. Leibniz composed the world of souls, and Hegelian Idealism says it is Mind. But Galileo and Newtonian science took the universe to be an inanimate machine.

Here then is an important problem. On what basis, experimental or intuitional, should a scientist choose his picture of the universe? As observation of animals does not necessarily imply that the universe is an animal–David Hume suggested that it was a cabbage–so experimentation with marbles does not imply that it is a machine. Indeed, can acquaintance with any part of the universe justify a conclusion true for the universe as a whole? Is one analogy any better than another? It was an unfortunate blindness to philosophical and logical problems that caused the eighteenth and nineteenth centuries to trouble themselves less and less about the logic of analogy. Those who boasted of science were certain that the universe with man in it is a machine.

These arguments, then, undermine the confidence of Clifford, Carlson, and Russell. Mechanism is not the scientific discovery of a fixed and final truth, nor is any law of physics a description of how nature works. This much can be asserted strictly within the limits of the Newtonian era. When now we come to the scientific revolution of the twentieth century, not only are these conclusions confirmed, but we are introduced to a radically new view, not merely of the accuracy of particular laws, but of the nature, the limitations, the purpose and significance of science as a whole.

Chapter Three

The Twentieth Century

The best-known fact about twentieth-century physics is its tremendous advance beyond everything that has preceded. Popularly, this advance is recognized in the use of television, jet planes, and the atomic bomb. But there is also some awareness on the part of the public that these inventions depend on new laws of physics, recently "discovered." Nearly everyone has heard of relativity and Einstein. There is a fairly wide apprehension that physics has undergone a revolution. Naturally, the scientists have a more ample appreciation of the scope of this revolution than does the general public; and for this reason they are more willing to admit that science does not discover absolute truth. If the earlier scientists had really discovered a law, it would not now be rejected. Fixed and final truth is not to be discarded. Therefore, the Aristotelian and Medieval notion, adopted by the Newtonian epigoni, that the laws of science are permanently beyond question has to a large measure been replaced by the Platonic and more skeptical view that all science is tentative.

This point presupposes that the revolution in science is not a mere addition of newly discovered laws to the laws previously discovered, but rather is a rejection of the earlier laws and their replacement with different laws. To support this point, therefore, it is necessary to continue with some more history and exposition. And the first example will be the simplest possible.

The Collapse of Mechanics

Newton's first law of motion, and the foundation on which all the rest of his system is based, is the law of inertia: "Every body continues in its state of rest, or of uniform motion in a straight line, unless it is compelled to change that state by forces impressed upon it." The difficulty with forces impressed on the planets has already been discussed; now the conception of uniform motion in a straight line requires attention. A study of astronomy causes one to wonder whether there is any such thing as motion in a straight line. What evidence is there of such a motion? Or, indeed, how could motion in a straight line be defined?

In colloquial language, a billiard ball is said to move in a straight line if it does not diverge from the shortest path between its present position and a fixed point on the table at which it arrives a moment later. A straight line, therefore, is determined by two points, one of which is the present position of the body in motion. But what about the other point, the so-called fixed point? Whether the case be that of a billiard ball or of a plane flying from New York to Los Angeles, the motion is not truly a straight line even if the moving bodies head constantly toward their destinations. During the time elapsed (this is more obvious but not more real in the case of the plane), the earth rotates and revolves. Therefore, Los Angeles is constantly changing its position in Newtonian space.

"Absolute space," said Newton, "in its own nature, without relation to anything external, remains always similar and immovable."

Now, if a goal is constantly changing its position in space, a body that is always moving toward it cannot move in a straight line. This that is true of the plane and Los Angeles is just as true of an atom in the interstellar spaces. If the motion of this atom could be observed to be in the direction of a "fixed" star, the motion could not be motion in a straight line, for the star is not fixed. It moves too, like Los Angeles. As there are no visible points in the heavens other than the stars, it remains forever impossible to discover a straight motion, if indeed there is one. Perhaps the planet Mars is moving in a perfectly straight line toward some invisible, hypothetical point in space, carrying the whole solar system along with it; but if it is, we could never know it because we cannot fix that point. Therefore, the idea of rectilinear motion must be dropped from science.

Since this first law of motion, the law of inertia, underlies the entire Newtonian system, a flaw at this point automatically alters all that follows.

Essentially the same difficulty attaches to Newton's concept of rest. The first part of the law had stated that a body continues at rest unless impressed forces compel a change. Can there be such a body? How could one identify it? Newton wrote (Scholium after Definition VIII),

> Absolute motion is the translation of a body from one absolute place into another; relative motion, the translation from one relative place into another. . . . But real absolute rest is the continuance of the body in the same part of that immovable space. . . . But we may distinguish rest and motion, absolute and relative, one from the other by their properties, causes, and effects. It is a property of rest, that bodies really at rest do rest in respect to one another. And therefore as it is possible that in the remote regions of the fixed stars, or perhaps far beyond them, there may be some body absolutely at rest; but impossible to know, from the position of bodies to one another in our regions, whether any of these do keep the same

> position to that remote body, it follows that absolute rest cannot be determined from the position of bodies in our regions.

Thus Newton himself acknowledged that it was impossible to identify any body as being absolutely at rest, but it is not likely that he remotely suspected the impossible situation he had created.

Absolute rest, absolute motion, and the absolute space in which they are supposed to occur lead to a further interesting ramification of the theory. Near the beginning of his *Principia,* Newton, who was so careful to define *mass, momentum,* etc., said, "I do not define *time, space, place,* and *motion,* as being well known to all." But he did insist on the distinction between absolute and relative motion, absolute and relative space, and absolute and relative time.

These absolutes are not in good scientific repute today, and Newton's defense of absolute motion has been adversely criticized. Newton's experiment had been ingenious. Cause a bucket of water to rotate rapidly. Newton used a rope and twisted it so that it would produce a revolution when he let go of the bucket. As the bucket just begins to rotate, the surface of the water remains level for a time; but after a little the bucket communicates its motion to the water. Not only does the water begin to rotate, it will climb up the side of the bucket, leaving the center depressed so that its surface is concave. On the basis of this experiment, Newton argued that when the *relative* motion of the water was greatest–that is, before the bucket had communicated its rotation to the water–the water remained level. Therefore the true or absolute motion of the water had not yet begun. But afterwards, when the *relative* motion of the water was least–that is when the water was also rotating–the rising of the water up the side of the bucket shows an endeavor to recede from the axis; and this endeavor reveals the real motion of the water, continually increasing, till it reaches its greatest point, when *relatively* the water is at rest in the bucket.

Ernst Mach *(Science of Mechanics,* Open Court, 1942, 280) replied,

> When quite modern authors let themselves be led astray by the Newtonian arguments which are derived from the bucket of water, to distinguish between relative and absolute motion, they do not reflect that the system of the world is only given *once* to us, and that the Ptolemaic or Copernican view is our interpretation, but both are equally actual. Try to fix Newton's bucket and rotate the heaven of fixed stars and then prove the absence of centrifugal forces!

Concerning Mach's reply, Hans Reichenbach (*Modern Philosophy of Science,* 50) adds, "Mach's answer is based on the fact that centrifugal force can be interpreted relativistically as a dynamic effect of gravitation produced by the rotation of the fixed stars." On the same subject of absolute motion, though not the bucket experiment, Reichenbach had just said,

> Perhaps no other passage so clearly demonstrates the tragic influence of Newton's philosophy upon his judgment. ... After two centuries of error, "philosophia naturalis" has finally abandoned Newton's philosophical views, but this does not detract from Newton's contributions to physics. Fortunately, all empirically grounded knowledge is independent of the interpretation of its discoverers, but the price of this independence is that such knowledge holds only approximately.

This last sentence puts the price too low, but the whole quotation plus Mach's argument is evidence that the Newtonian system is no longer accepted.

The extension of the argument against absolute motion to the concepts of absolute time and space may be indicated by an additional reference to Mach and Reichenbach. The former argues that

> time is an abstraction at which we arrive by means of the changes of things. . . . A motion may, with respect to another motion, be uniform. But the question whether a motion is *in itself* uniform, is senseless. With just as little justice, also, may we speak of an "absolute time"–of a time independent of change [*Science of Mechanics,* 272].

The latter's argument appears in an incisive analysis that is too complicated to be reproduced here, but the rejection of absolute space is centered in the statement, "Space is the order of co-existing things, or the order of existence for all things which are contemporaneous" (*The Theory of Motion, According to Newton, Leibniz, and Huyghens,* 52).

These analyses of the absolutes of space and time may seem to be more philosophic than strictly scientific, if such a distinction retains any appreciable meaning. But no such objection, however superficial it may be, can be raised against recent investigations of velocity and light. These can be offered as the convincing, laboratory, experimental proof that Newtonian mechanics has collapsed.

Newton's formulations presuppose the possibility of determining the position and the velocity of a particle absolutely, that is, apart from its relation to any other particle. At the same time the law of gravitation asserts the continuous interaction of all particles. For a long time the incompatibility of these two presuppositions did not hinder the brilliant development of Newtonian science, and proud scientists dismissed the logical analysis as the ethereal speculations of nebulous philosophers;* but when in the very recent past the phenomena of light became more frequent factors in experimentation, the latent contradiction soon resulted in the destruction of the noble edifice.

An electron, so our contemporary experts tell us, can be studied only as it interchanges energy with some other thing. In complete isolation it could never be discovered. Now, an electron is so slight a body (if it is a body) that any exchange of energy seriously disturbs it. Even light disturbs it. If in studying the electron we use light of long wavelength and little energy, the disturbance may be small and the velocity of the electron would hardly be changed; but the picture would be so hazy that we could not determine the position of the electron. On the other hand, if we use light of a short wavelength and greater energy, and so are able to determine the electron's position, its motion becomes unpredictable. That is to say, the more accurately we determine its position, the less accurately we can determine its velocity; and the more accurately we determine its velocity, the less we can determine its position. But for scientific prediction, which was earlier seen to be one of the most important features distinguishing modern from ancient science, velocity and position

* Hans Reichenbach, *Modern Philosophy of Science,* 46-47, gives another example of the failure of scientists to profit from philosophical analysis. "It is ironic," he says, "that Newton, who enriched science so immensely by his physical discoveries, at the same time largely hindered the development of its conceptual foundation. . . . His theory of mechanics arrested the analysis of space and time for more than two centuries, despite the fact that Leibniz, who was his contemporary, had demonstrated a much deeper understanding of the nature of space and time. . . . The injustice of history goes even further; . . . [his] theories seem to have been forgotten by the scientists and to have been preserved only by the historians of philosophy. . . . Mach, the first relativist of the new era . . . did not know anything of Leibniz' well-grounded objections to Newton, and made only a few naive comments about him. Even Einstein's solution, going far beyond Mach, took Newton's 'classical mechanics' as his starting point without any reference to Leibniz and Huyghens." One might also mention Percy Bridgman's statement in *The Way Things Are* (134), "The vision that it may be conceptually illegitimate to extend indefinitely the world revealed to us by instrumentation [as Lorentz did in his theory of the electron] is one that we owe to recent quantum theory." No, it is not. It is the old logical fallacy of composition and division, revealed to students in elementary logic textbooks.

must both be accurately known.

This is enough to demonstrate that mechanistic determinism is not a discovery based on observation, but an *a priori* thesis adopted for other reasons. Whether or not this is enough to demonstrate that nature is indeterministic is quite a different question. But enough or not, it is not all. Experimentation with light has produced further astounding results. The story has often been told before, but for the present purpose it must be repeated, of how the nineteenth century disproved Newton's corpuscular theory of light by a crucial experiment, which once and for all established the wave theory and put it beyond all future doubt.

From the mechanics of fluids it follows that the speed of light in air would be greater than in water, if light is a wave-motion in a medium; but the speed of light would be greater in water, if light is corpuscular. Unfortunately, in Newton's day there was no method for making these measurements, and Newton himself recognized the need of further experimentation. Arago outlined the necessary experiment in 1838, and in 1850 Leon Foucault carried it out. He discovered thereby that the speed of light is greater in air.

From a strictly logical point of view this experimental discovery would not establish the wave theory, unless waves and corpuscles were the only alternatives. Since no other possibility was then known, most people concluded that the wave theory was established. What they were more sure of was that the corpuscular theory had been permanently disproved. If this theory requires light to travel faster in water, and it in fact does not, then the corpuscular theory must be false, permanently false.

Astoundingly enough, another so-called crucial experiment was performed in 1902 by Phillip Lenard, and its significance was seen by Einstein in 1905. Suppose a source of light shines upon a copper plate: The energy set up in the plate per unit of time can be measured. If the distance between the plate and the source of light is gradually increased, the amount of energy decreases. Now, on the assumption that light is a wave-motion, this decrease continues infinitely toward zero. If, however, light is a particle, and the source emits so many particles per unit of time, the decrease will not decrease uniformly to zero because the energy absorbed by the plate can never be less than the energy of a single particle. The experiment showed that the energy does not decrease uniformly toward zero, but on the contrary decreases to one and then drops suddenly to zero. Hence the wave theory seems to have been proved false, permanently false.

At this point we must pause to clarify the logic both of this particular situation and of experimental verification in general. A simple argument of verification proceeds as follows: The given hypothesis implies certain definite results; the experiment actually gives these results; therefore, the hypothesis is verified and can be called a law. Obviously, this argument is the fallacy of asserting the consequent; and since all verification must commit this fallacy, it follows that no law or hypothesis can ever be logically demonstrated.

It seems, however, that hypotheses can be logically proven false. The argument would go: The given hypothesis implies certain definite results; the experiment actually gives a contradictory result; therefore the hypothesis is false. Obviously, this is the perfectly valid argument of denying the consequent. So it would seem that although laws can be proven false, they can never be proven true.

Nonetheless, there are complications, and the situation which inspired this elementary lesson in logic is an excellent example. The strict argument in 1850 should have been: The corpuscular theory of light plus all Newtonian mechanics implies what the experiment denied; therefore, either the corpuscular theory is false or something is wrong with Newtonian mechanics, or both. But at that date no one was willing to question Newtonian mechanics. The later experiment of Lenard as well as Einstein's argumentation show that light may consist of particles if we discard Newtonian mechanics. And today the Newtonian laws have been replaced.

Strangely enough, scientists today use both theories of light. For some purposes, they say light is a wave motion; for other purposes, they say light consists of particles. Obviously these two theories cannot both be true. But they both prove useful, and contemporary scientists sometimes display puckish glee in their little inconsistencies: As one brilliant scientist explained it, light is not a wave, not a particle, but a wavicle.

Nor are the two theories of light the only example of the self-contradictory state of science. Experiments on the thermal properties of gases use a theory that pictures a gas as an aggregate of discrete particles; but in acoustics, the scientist represents gas as a continuous medium. Logically, these theories cannot both be true, and one is led to conclude that the violation of logic can be justified only on the ground that scientists are not interested in the literal truth of their laws.

But if the logic of the situation is easily determined, the science of the situation is somewhat obscure. That Newtonian mechanics has collapsed is not obscure. If the relatively simple items mentioned do not suffice to convince a man, let him read the new formula for the addition of velocities,* the change of mass into energy and back again, the dependence of length on velocity, the problem of simultaneity, and a long list of modern marvels. What remains obscure are the particular laws that science will propose next, and whether any scientific law will ever again enjoy as much as two centuries or even two decades of acceptance. Science changes with ever increasing rapidity. The dogmatic assertion of absolute truths, the exclusion of all non-observational data, the idea that science really discovers how nature works have been amply refuted. What is needed now is not so much a new science, but a new philosophy of science. And attempts in this direction are not lacking.

* The case of the addition of velocities provides an easily understood refutation of an attempt to rehabilitate Newton and the discovery of absolute truth. It has been said that the newer laws are simply more accurate descriptions and that the earlier laws are special cases deducible from the more general laws later discovered. Morris R. Cohen,

Operationalism

In the latter years of the nineteenth century, there were two groups of philosophical scientists. One group, against whom this argument has been directed, stressed the results and contents of science and erected ultimate principles of nature, life, and religion upon them. If these writers were not all narrowly materialists, they were at least naturalists. The second group, even if some of its members made and still make naturalistic assertions, stressed the methods of science and dismissed questions of ultimate principles as metaphysical pseudo-problems. These writers are now known as logical positivists.

Perhaps we should locate the origin of logical positivism in Ernst Mach (1838-1916). He argued against a materialistic as well as against a mentalistic metaphysics. But whether he opposed all metaphysics, as the logical positivists now do, is doubtful, because of his assertion that reality is neutral. In any case, this assertion is singularly uninformative and does not go beyond Lange's and Kant's unknowable. *Neutral* means simply

The Meaning of Human History, 85-86, has it this way: "Can we formulate an accurate universal proposition (i.e, one without any exception) that will enable us to tell what is relevant and what is irrelevant to all these motions? The law of gravitation does precisely this. . . . Another law such as Einstein's may replace it as a more accurate description, but such another law will have to include the truth of the older one under restricted conditions." Cohen also specifies the laws of light as examples. But Cohen is mistaken. The formula $v_1 + v_2 = V$ *(i.e.,* a man who walks 3 MPH forward in a train traveling 60 MPH is moving forward 63 MPH) cannot be mathematically deduced from and as a special case of:

$$V = \frac{v_1 + v_2}{1 + \frac{v_1 v_2}{C^2}}$$

Of course, the square of the speed of light is a negligible quantity in walking forward in a train; but this is not the consideration by which one equation is determined as a special case of another.

neither mental nor material. But what positively it is, or even what alternatives there are, Mach and Lange cannot say. These people are often the first to complain about the meaninglessness of negative theology. Eternity is taken to be a mere denial of time without any positive content. But to say that reality is neutral is just as negative and just as meaningless.

The later followers of Mach try to be more consistent. They definitely disallow all metaphysics. No statement about reality is to be permitted. Ultimate reality is an empty and useless concept; or, rather, it is a word without a concept. Questions about the soul, even questions about the origin of life, are pseudo-problems. Every meaningful proposition (except the formal, procedural tautologies of logic and mathematics) must be verified by sensory observation. A statement that cannot be related to and tested by scientific experiment says nothing. Thus both God and matter are nonsense syllables. An extension of this viewpoint brings us to operationalism.

In the United States, one of the early and most prominent advocates of operationalism was Percy Bridgman *(The Logic of Modern Physics,* 1927). Although his book is intensely interesting, it is, however, impossible to give a complete account of it here. The present aim is to characterize and project a trend of thought. For this purpose it is not necessary to do full justice to Bridgman, much less to agree with all he says. Indeed one may hold that Bridgman does not consistently carry through with his main theses. At any rate, the situation in science, which Bridgman so well describes in other respects, does not seem to justify his assertion, "The attitude of the physicist must therefore be one of pure empiricism" (3). Hence, the present purpose is to select those ideas which constitute Bridgman's most useful contribution and to press them perhaps beyond the limits he himself would impose.

As a student, Bridgman received a Newtonian education, and he acknowledges that "It was a great shock to discover that classical concepts, accepted unquestioningly, were inadequate to meet the actual situation" (1). In the Introduction (ix) he anticipates the extent of the shock by saying,

> The experimental facts are so utterly different from those of our ordinary experience that not only do we apparently have to give up generalizations from past experience as broad as the field equations of electrodynamics, for instance, but it is even being questioned whether our ordinary forms of thought are applicable in the new domain; it is often suggested, for example, that the concepts of space and time break down.

Although this monograph's argument has shown the impossibility of a pure empiricism by indicating some factors that are not observational data, one of Bridgman's main reasons for his unfortunate generalization is quite sound. He insists that the concepts proper in a given type of experiment must not be assumed as applicable to another range of experience. Rather than anticipating it with old concepts, one must wait for the further experience, and only then decide on what concepts to use.

This general principle is discussed at length under the picturesque notion of the penumbra. After remarking that all results of measuring are only approximate and that therefore statements about numerical relations between measured quantities are valid only with limits, Bridgman concludes, "We never have clean cut knowledge of anything, but all our experience is surrounded by a twilight zone, a penumbra of uncertainty, into which we have not penetrated" (33). Concerning what is there and what goes on in this penumbra, one must hold no preconceived notions. Even

> arithmetic, so far as it purports to deal with actual physical objects, is also affected with the same

> penumbra of uncertainty. . . . If the statement of arithmetic is to be an exact statement in the mathematical sense, the "object" must be a definite clean-cut thing, which preserves its identity in time with no penumbra. But this sort of thing is never experienced, and far as we know does not correspond exactly to anything in experience. . . . Even solids [not to mention liquids and gases] evaporate, or condense gases on them, and we see that an object with identity is an abstraction corresponding exactly to nothing in nature [34-35].

Bridgman finds the same sort of penumbra present in physical explanations also: "An explanation is not an absolute sort of thing, but what is satisfactory for one man will not be for another" (38). Explanations depend on the elements or axioms used, and these depend on the purpose in view, and also on the range of our previous physical experience. Therefore, explanations change as the physicist progresses.

> In the realm of quantum phenomena it is of course the merest commonplace that our old ideas of mechanics and electrodynamics have failed, so that it is a matter of the greatest concern to find how many, or indeed whether any, elements of the old situations can be carried over into the new [41].

Many physicists in the past have not observed this caution. Confronted with something new, they usually devised a structure built out of familiar elements and used it to explain what lay beyond their actual range of experimentation. But, asserts Bridgman, "There is no warrant whatever in experience for the conviction that as we penetrate deeper and deeper we shall find the elements of previous experience repeated" (43-44). Faraday and, to a lesser extent, Maxwell were guilty of this unwarranted extension of concepts when they tried to explain electricity by mechanical pushes and pulls. An earlier and more horrible example was Boscovitch in his attempt to explain gravitation. Bridgman waxes emphatic: "It is difficult to conceive anything more scientifically bigoted than to postulate that all possible experience conforms to the same type as that with which we are familiar" (46). A longing for mechanical explana-tion, he says, has all the tenacity of original sin.

The implication of this line of reasoning is that we should analyze nature into correlations without any assumption whatever as to the character of these correlations. We must accept as an ultimate for explanation the mere statement of a correlation.

On considerations such as these, Bridgman calls into question the existence of electric fields. Nearly every physicist assumes that a field of force is a physical reality.

> The reality of the field is self-consciously inculcated in our elementary teaching . . . and is considered the most fundamental concept of all modem electrical theory. Yet in spite of this, I believe that a critical examination will show that the ascription of physical reality to the electric field is entirely without justification. I cannot find a single physical phenomenon or a single physical operation by which evidence of the existence of the field may be obtained independent of the operations which entered the definition [57].

In addition to all this, which may be called negative and destructive, Bridgman offers a positive proposal for the formulation of the concepts of physics. His first example is the simplest possible–the concept of length. For virtually all physicists in the past, length has been a real physical characteristic of a real individual object. It was something that we could see before our very eyes. But if, as a previous quotation from Bridgman has already indicated, there is no such thing as a real individual object, the concept of length must be otherwise understood. "What do we mean," he says,

> by the *length* of an object? We evidently know what we mean by length if we can tell what the length of any and every object is, and for the physicist nothing more is required. To find the length of an object, we have to perform certain physical operations. The concept of length is therefore fixed when the operations by which length is measured are fixed: that is, the concept of length involves as much as and nothing more than the set of operations by which length is determined. In general, we mean by any concept nothing more than a set of operations; *the concept is synonymous with the corresponding set of operations* [italics his; 5].
>
> If we have more than one set of operations, we have more than one concept, and strictly there should be a separate name to correspond to each different set of operations [10].

He goes on to show that astronomical "length," naive, everyday "length," and microscopic "length" are three entirely different concepts.

> What is the possible meaning of the statement that the diameter of an electron is 10^{-13} centimeters? Again, the only answer is found by examining the operations by which the number 10^{-13} was obtained. This number came by solving certain equations derived from the field equations of electrodynamics, into which certain numerical data obtained by experience had been substituted. The concept of length has therefore

> now been so modified as to include that theory of electricity embodied in the field equations, and, most important, assumes the correctness of extending these equations from the dimensions in which they may be verified experimentally into a region in which their correctness is one of the most important and problematical of present-day questions in physics. . . . As a matter of fact, the concept of length disappears as an independent thing and fuses in a complicated way with other concepts, all of which are themselves altered thereby . . . [21-22].

The significance of this theory of the operational definition of concepts should not be missed. Length, mass, electric charge and all the concepts of physics are descriptions of operations performed in laboratories. They are not descriptions of natural objects or physical realities. The laws of physics, the equations embodying the concepts, do not describe how nature goes on. They describe how the physicist goes on. It would be most astounding if the processes of nature and the processes of the physicist were the same. On the contrary, the most certain truth of physics is that physics is not true–not true as an account of what nature is and how nature works. The concepts of physics are the operations of the physicist.

Since concepts change with the change of operations, it follows that when we investigate phenomena outside the domain of a previous experiment, it is always illegitimate to apply the concepts so obtained. A change of operations changes the concepts; and to use the same names in both cases, whether the name be *length, mass, time,* or *space,* is to flounder in ambiguity. What is worse, from the standpoint of the neatly ordered world of mechanism, is that concepts lose their individuality and fuse together as the experimental limits are approached. After his remarks on the dimensions of an electron, Bridgman concludes that "the concepts of length and the electric field vectors fuse into an amorphous whole" (24).

Bridgman further illustrates his views by an analysis of the concepts of space, time, cause, velocity, energy, and some others. Since the "length" of a meter stick is not the "length" of light waves, there are at least two different kinds of "space," tactual and optical. Similarly, there are two times. One time has to do with events taking place near each other in tactual space, and the other time relates to events astronomically separated from each other. From this, it also follows that time and space are inextricably mixed together. "This is not primarily a statement about nature at all, and might have been made simply by the observation that the operations by which extended time is measured involve those for measuring space" (69).

The complications are enormous.

> We recognize in principle that the length of the meter stick may be different when in motion, that it may change also during the acceleration incident to moving it from one place to another, and that until proved to the contrary the velocity of light may be a function of velocity or acceleration [70].

Complications such as these do not decrease when it is a question of force, mass, energy and thermodynamics. But to list the details is perhaps now unnecessary.

Bridgman also draws the conclusion that because of these considerations all our knowledge is relative. Here we need not follow him, for this is an invalid implication. Philosophical relativism does not follow from operationalism, and skepticism in science is not *ipso facto* a universal skepticism. Bridgman could have properly concluded that all knowledge derived by laboratory processes is relative; all the laws and concepts of physics are relative. But the conclusion he actually gives requires as a premise the *absolute* assertion that laboratory procedure is the sole gateway to all knowledge. This principle from Karl Pearson, however, lacks, as we have seen, empirical, scientific, observational justification. Perhaps Bridgman agrees with Pearson, but he has no experimental or operational basis for such agreement.

Not only does the scientism of Karl Pearson lack scientific support, the general assertion of philosophical relativism is self-destructive. When a philosopher asserts that all knowledge is relative, he fails to recognize that he violates his own principle by asserting it. This statement he never considers relative and tentative; this statement he never intends to replace by its contradictory. Hence, the relativists are absolutists in spite of themselves. But if relativism and skepticism are confined to science, the operationalists have won a complete victory over the dogmatic views of the Newtonian era.

Expressions of Skepticism

On a previous page this earlier, unyielding dogmatism was illustrated in a list of citations. Science made permanent discoveries of nature's workings, arrived at fixed truths, and formulated absolute judgments. Here is the appropriate place to include another list. In contrast to the former, the more recent scientists have recognized certain limitations of science and have entertained a greater or lesser degree of skepticism. The following quotations are examples of this skeptical tendency. It is not the aim to assess accurately the degree of skepticism for each author. Some of them, for example Sullivan, are on the whole less skeptical than they appear to be in the sentences selected. The aim, on the contrary, is simply to point out the trend of scientific thought and to emphasize the sharp contrast between the nineteenth and twentieth centuries.

The first in this list will be the final quotation from Bridgman, this time from one of his later publications, *The Way Things Are* (129).

> Some people go so far as to *define* science as the consensus of all competent observers. This it seems to me goes too far and misplaces the emphasis. . . . "Competent persons" at any epoch means those who at that epoch have been subjected to a definite preconditioning. . . . It does not preclude the possibility that all competent persons are reacting incorrectly because of some feature in contemporary culture, and there are examples, as Weierstrass in mathematics, where consensus was ultimately shown to have been wrong.

The quotation points up the wide possibility of error among scientists. The great majority may all be wrong. However, this is not a sufficient reason for refusing "to define science as the consensus of all competent observers." It merely means that science, as a description of nature, is usually, indeed always, mistaken.

Next, J. W. N. Sullivan in *The Limitations of Science* opposes the extremes of conventionalism and holds that objective, physical characters really exist in nature, quite independently of our methods of measuring them; and, apparently speaking for himself as well, he notes that most scientists still believe that there is a final scientific truth about the universe to which they are approximating (160-162). Nonetheless, this belief in a final scientific truth, he admits, is an article of faith; what the fundamental physical quantities of the universe are, nobody knows. This is a degree of skepticism never found in Büchner, for example.

In other passages, Sullivan seems even more skeptical. Pictorial representations of an electron are superseded by mathematical symbols, and we do not know what these symbols stand for in actual physical reality (38). On the next page, he even says that "truth" in science is convenience and that scientists are pragmatists in practice, whatever dogmatic philosophy they believe. And finally, paraphrasing somewhat freely, we do not need to know the nature of the entities we discuss; all we actually know about these entities is the way they affect our measuring instruments. Though we measure distances in space, it is evident that the space of physics has nothing to do with the space of perception. Since a mathematical web can always be woven about any distribution of objects, the fact that physics deals in mathematical structures may be a coincidence rather than a discovery. Sullivan questions whether energy is a constituent of the external universe and doubts that it never increases or diminishes. Bohr's picture of revolving electrons inside an atom was first thought to be faithful to objective reality; but now we realize that any other picture, consistent with the equations, would do as well. And the Schrödinger atom with its waves in multi-dimensional space is frankly incredible. Then, to conclude these selected phrases from Sullivan (38, 41, 141-162), we quote his assertion that "it is highly probable that all scientific theories are wrong."

Sullivan, like the present writer, is interested in defending certain ethical, aesthetic, and theological values from scientific annihilation. Philipp Frank *(Philosophy of Science,* 238-242) criticizes his argument as a gross oversimplification. Sullivan had argued: Since physicists do not know the nature of the entities they discuss, but know only the mathematical structures, science cannot insist that only matter in motion is real and that God and morality are unreal. Frank objects that some later Newtonians denied the reality of matter and maintained that only energy is real, and this kind of physics allows room for values. Or, contrariwise, continues Frank, "it is hardly more plausible to regard beauty and communion with God as de Broglie waves than to regard them as material masses."

The last sentence and the theme it expresses are quite true. One cannot defend spiritual realities simply by replacing matter in motion with de Broglie waves. Nor, to refer to other authors, can one defend free will by quantum theory, or predestination by relativity. But perhaps Frank has misunderstood Sullivan's argument. To the extent that Sullivan retains some nineteenth-century dogmatism, he may be open to criticism. But it can apply only to the extent that physics grasps absolute truth.

To what extent does Frank think that physics grasps absolute truth? On an earlier page he admits,

> It took a long time for the present day theory of motion to develop, and we do not know now whether or not it is the right scheme for the future. . . . It is very important to appreciate correctly that the old theories had their own logical consistency and beauty. We cannot say that the people who believed them were "wrong," but it is certain that they used a different symbolic scheme [90].

Here Frank seems fairly skeptical: We cannot say that the present theory is right nor that ancient theories were wrong. In the first sentence the phrase "we do not know now" leaves open the possibility that we may arrive at absolute truth someday, but the remainder is skeptical in tendency.

However, in criticizing Sullivan, Frank seems to adopt a more dogmatic attitude. He writes, "One can clearly see that the word 'uncertainty' in Heisenberg's principle does not mean 'uncertainty' about the truth of a scientific theory" (241). This indeed is true; one can be quite certain that sub-atomic motion is uncertain or unpredictable. But Frank apparently does not see that Sullivan's argument contains no such confusion. Sullivan does not argue: Since de Broglie waves have replaced atomic particles, we may believe in ethical and theological values. The argument is rather this: Since the advance of science from atoms to de Broglie waves and other modern marvels shows that physical laws are only tentative, that they are not descriptions of nature or statements about ultimate reality; since indeed scientists have no knowledge of the natural entities they discuss; and since it is highly probable that all scientific theories are wrong, science cannot insist that God and morality are unreal. Frank's objection to this argument is completely beside the point.

Bridgman and Sullivan have now been quoted as tending toward scientific skepticism. To them might be added a number of scientists, Frank included, who admit that aesthetic preferences–particularly in respect to mathematical simplicity–determine the most general equations a scientist accepts. No discovery of physical truth is involved; it is merely a matter of beauty and elegance.

Nor is aesthetics the only non-observational determinant of physical law. C. West Churchman, not a skeptic by any means, writes, "The simplest question of fact in science requires for even an approximation a judgment of value . . . the science of ethics (like all the principal branches of science) is *basic* [italics his] to the meaning of any question the experimental scientist raises" *(Theory of Experimental Inference,* vii). Without pressing the question as to how ethical norms are established, it would seem that a choice of physical laws on the basis of ethical principles represents a skeptical tendency in physics.

Objections to Operationalism

Admittedly, the theory of operationalism and its skeptical implications are not universally accepted by twentieth-century scientists and philosophers. Several writers attempt to maintain some attentuated form of dogmatism. A. R. Hall *(The Scientific Revolution,* xi) insists that science deals with

> material entities in nature, . . . distinguishes firmly between theories confirmed by multiple evidence, tentative hypotheses, and unsupported speculations. It presents, not a possible or even a plausible picture of nature, but one in which all available facts are given their logical, orderly places.

While the remainder of the book is informative and interesting, Hall seems to rest in naive confidence and makes no attempt to meet the skeptical arguments.

Hans Reichenbach, previously quoted, does better. The chapter on rationalism and empiricism in *Modern Philosophy of Science* goes to some length in defending the older attitude toward science. In answer to Hume, Reichenbach makes two points. First, he redefines knowledge and truth so as to preserve "knowledge" in science. It could perhaps be argued that what he now takes to be "knowledge" is not far removed from skepticism. But his second point can be more quickly handled. He seems to interpret the force of Hume's arguments as casting doubt only on the accuracy of predictions concerning the future (142). This is a patently inadequate interpretation of Hume. Hume's philosophy rules out all inductions and generalizations of the past as well.

There are two other authors who meet operationalism head-on and in detail. It is necessary, therefore, to consider seriously the objections of A. Cornelius Benjamin and Ernest Nagel.

Professor Benjamin *(Operationism,* 1955) gives a thoughtful and extended criticism of Bridgman. Of its two main thrusts, one accuses Bridgman of inconsistency in minor particulars, while the other rejects the theory in its most generalized form.

As for the minor particulars, Benjamin quotes Bridgman's inconsistent (or at least unrelated) definitions of his method. There is a narrow sense of the term *operation,* referring to physical measurement by meter sticks, and a wider sense including mental, that is, pencil and paper, operations. Bridgman's failure to distinguish symbolic from non-symbolic operations, his failure to classify operations (or even to list their types exhaustively) Benjamin takes to be a fatal confusion.

Gustav Bergmann also notes this difficulty *(Philosophy of Science,* 58):

> While operations in the relevant sense are manipulations and nothing else, the "operationists"

> saw operations everywhere. At one extreme, the scientist's observations were decked out to be a species of operations; at the other, his verbal and computational activities were, as so-called symbolic operations, herded into the same corral. Such completely non-specific use of "operation" (or of any word) is not only useless; it is also confusing.

Bergmann's continuation of this objection specifies John Dewey as another example. Yet it is not clear that this is such a fatal and irremediable flaw as Benjamin thinks. John Dewey may be confusing, and Bridgman may have been inconsistent. In fact it seems that he was, for in addition to his main assertion, "The concept is synonymous with the corresponding operations," he also said, "The operational aspect is not by any means the only aspect of meanings." However, this is not a fatal and final objection to operationalism, for confusions are avoidable and inconsistencies are removable.

Now, it is not surprising that Bridgman's early work, *The Logic of Modern Physics* (1927), should contain several minor infelicities. Even in a later work where he replies directly to Benjamin *(The Way Things Are,* 37-38), he does not fully meet the criticisms. But the significance of this is of small importance for the present purpose and even perhaps for Bridgman also, because, on the one hand, the lesser details can be adjusted and made harmonious, while, on the other, the criticism applies to an extended and generalized theory of operationalism that leaves the narrower domain of physics and merges with general epistemology.

Benjamin admits that Bridgman disclaims any general theory of knowledge and ostensibly restricts himself to physics and its technique. But, asserts the critic, epistemological postulates underlie such a restricted view even if Bridgman does not state them. On this point, Benjamin is quite right. We too admit that in one place Bridgman actually asserted a general epistemological relativism, and that, as Benjamin claims, he and his followers incline to pragmatism and logical positivism. Benjamin certainly has a point. But it is a point that can be avoided, no doubt in opposition to Bridgman's inclinations, by insisting on the narrower view of operationalism and combining it with an epistemology foreign to both authors.

Let us therefore confine our argument to Benjamin's specific objections to the narrower form of operationalism. He holds that the thesis, "Concepts are synonymous with physical operations," is refuted very simply: It is false as a description of techniques, futile as a proposal for the future, and patently absurd!

Just why Benjamin declares operationalism false and futile is not easy to see, unless it is because he includes these two points under the rubric of "patently absurd." On this third point, Benjamin argues that each operation is a singular, datable event and cannot be repeated. Therefore, no two operations can give the same concept. Hence, in measuring a desk by a meter stick, there would be different concepts–not merely different lengths, but different concepts of length–each time the desk was measured, even by the same meter stick. And most people would agree that this is patently absurd.

Rather clearly, however, this absurdity is not Bridgman's meaning. In these several attempts to measure the desk, a meter stick is always used. Though the results in centimeters may differ, the method or operation is the same, and therefore there is but one concept of length involved. Only when meter sticks are replaced by electron microscopes or other instruments does a different concept appear. And this is not patently absurd.

Instead of envisaging the description of techniques and showing that operationalism is false on this count, Benjamin's objection does not really concern operationalism as a narrow theory of physics, but as a general epistemology. For it is in this connection that Benjamin charges Bridgman with an over-emphasis on particularity. Bridgman, in making operations singular, datable, unrepeatable events, has, in Benjamin's opinion, provided no method of developing abstract concepts from the singular experiments. In other words, Bridgman is an extreme nominalist: There is nothing similar in any two applications of a meter stick. Now, the problem of universals is, of course, a substantial epistemological problem; but this is hardly a sufficient reason for claiming that operationalism is false as a description of techniques in physics. Let it be admitted that Bridgman, the physicist, is weak in epistemology; yet the method of measuring by meter sticks is nonetheless an abstract or universal concept distinguishable from microscopic techniques that give rise to a different concept of length.

Benjamin also repeats Franz Adler's *reductio ad absurdum:* to define C_n, add the number of hours a man sleeps on a given night to the length of his nose, plus or minus one for whether he likes or dislikes fried liver, etc.; repeat the measurements every Monday as long as you can, and juggle the figures into some mathematical formula. Thus the concept C_n is a carefully devised scientific concept.

Very witty, but this is not a *reductio ad absurdum* of operationalism. If it reduces anything to absurdity, it is all science that it makes absurd. Even in the strictest Newtonianism, there is no guarantee against multiplying the diameter of the Earth by the periodicity of the tides, dividing by pi, and correlating the result with the speed of light in water and in air. Both examples are absurd in the sense of useless. And the operationalist, as easily as the Newtonian, can drop such experiments and try to find other and more useful concepts.

Running through Benjamin's criticism is another theme more clearly expressed by Professor Nagel. It has to do with objectivity, the truth value of scientific laws, and their reference to nature. Nagel notes *(The Structure of Science,* 137) that proponents of instrumentalism or operationalism believe that thus scientific theories are shown to be improper subjects for the characterizations of true and false. Such is admittedly the argument of this monograph. Nagel then adds that there is no necessary incompatibility between saying that a theory is true and saying it is useful. This, too, we grant. But it is irrelevant because the basic question is whether a scientific theory can be true. The main problem faces in the opposite direction. It is this: Since, as has been shown, the laws of physics cannot be true–that is, true as descriptions of how an independent nature works–what then is their status? Operationalism or instrumentalism answers this question.

The flaw in the criticism of both Benjamin and Nagel is their ineradicable assurance that science must be true and must compel the assent of all unprejudiced investigators. Thus Nagel continues that the operationalists do not agree in their accounts of "scientific objects," such as electrons and light waves, which are ostensibly postulated by microscopic theories. If this be a sound objection to operationalism, it must apply to non-operationalistic scientists as well, for these too disagree in their accounts of electrons and light waves. Then Nagel adds, "But the further point [it is not a further point, but the same one over again] can also be made that it is far from clear how, on this view, such 'scientific objects' can be said to be physically existing things" (140). But who said it? Not Bridgman. Nor this monograph. Electrons and light waves are not physically existing things; they are elements of a set of instructions on how to operate in a laboratory. Now, if some halfhearted operationalists have discussed the question whether atoms exist and have concluded that they do, as Nagel suggests, this unfortunate inconsistency in a few writers is not a refutation of the wholehearted theory.

Conclusion

For a conclusion, we shall propose, first, that the expressions of skepticism be taken very seriously. In the Introduction, a contemporary scientist was quoted to the effect that he was completely baffled by the fact that when one picks up one end of a pencil, the other end comes along with it. This enigma depends on the distances between the atoms that make up the pencil and the more immense distances between the mysterious protons and neutrons that make up the atom. Ninety-nine percent or more of the space between the two ends of the pencil is completely empty; and experience teaches that if we pick up a dozen grains of sand at the end of a line of such grains, the rest of the line does not come along. Science, then, has no knowledge of what happens when we pick up a pencil.

Though this example comes from the twentieth century, a similar ignorance characterized the Newtonian era, even if the dogmatic scientists were ignorant of their ignorance. David Hume gave the example of two smooth pieces of marble that adhere together in such a manner as to require great force to separate them in a direct line, though they make so small a resistance to a lateral pressure.

The present writer asked three physicists about this problem. The first explained the phenomenon by air pressure and vacuum. The smooth surfaces prevent any air from remaining between the pieces of marble. They are hard to separate because the air pressure on the outside holds them together. The second physicist explained that when the surfaces are very smooth, the two faces are so close to each other that a molecular attraction is set up similar to that inside any single piece of marble. To separate the pieces is almost as hard as to pull a single piece apart. I asked this gentleman if air pressure had anything to do with the phenomenon. He confidently asserted that air pressure was entirely irrelevant. Molecular attraction is the explanation. The third physicist answered simply that nobody knows why the pieces adhere. I am inclined to believe he was right.

Therefore, the first point of this conclusion is to reassert Hume's statement,

> The utmost effort of human reason is to reduce the principles, productive of natural phenomena, to a greater simplicity, and to resolve the many particular effects into a few general causes, by means of reasonings from analogy, experience, and observation. But as to the causes of these general causes, we should in vain attempt their discovery; nor shall we ever be able to satisfy ourselves, by any particular explication of them. These ultimate springs and principles are totally shut up from human curiosity and enquiry [*Enquiry,* Section IV, Part I].

The second point of the conclusion complements the first. The bare assertion that science leaves us in ignorance of the workings of nature is not a sufficient philosophy of science. Something must be said of the nature and use of science. Therefore, operationalism is offered, not as a general theory of epistemology, but as the best available philosophy of science. It is a better statement of what science is, what science actually does, and what science can do.

Only by denying that science is cognitive can one justify the use of contradictory theories. For all the witty remarks about wavicles, two irreducible equations cannot both describe the propagation of light. No sane person can accept them both as accurate descriptions of nature. But if science, instead of being regarded as cognitive, is taken as a method for dominating and utilizing nature, then there is nothing reprehensible in using these incompatible formulas.

Just above, Professor Nagel made the perfectly correct but completely irrelevant point that a formula can be both true and useful. At this stage nearly everyone will see that the relevant question is, Can a formula be false and also useful? It can.

An interesting example is the reduction of mortality in cows with milk fever. The germ theory of disease, newly discovered by Louis Pasteur, led a Danish veterinarian to inject an antiseptic solution into the cows' udders. Mortality fell from ninety to thirty percent. This seemed to confirm the germ theory of disease, until it was discovered that distilled water produced as many cures as the antiseptic solution. Later, compressed air did even better. Operationalism will accept the procedures as useful, but the theories of how nature works in milk fever were false.

Science, then, must not be regarded as cognitive, but rather as an attempt to utilize nature for our needs and wants. This philosophy of science is not put forward as a general epistemology, and most certainly not as a universal relativism. Universal relativism is self-stultifying. On the contrary, operationalism is here offered absolutely as a philosophy of science. Instead of being the sole gateway to all knowledge, science is not a way to any knowledge–unless, as was just said, it is a knowledge of what to do in a laboratory. But knowledge of nature, No. To repeat a previous quotation from Bridgman, "This [bit of physics] is not primarily a statement about nature at all."

The third point of the conclusion is that the relationship between science, on the one hand, and religion, morals, and other normative disciplines, on the other, must be construed in terms radically different from the views of Büchner, Clifford, Carlson, and those of like mind. Scientific naturalism, that is, naturalism offered as an inescapable conclusion of science, must be repudiated.

In his presidential address before the American Philosophical Association in 1954, Ernest Nagel said,

> The occurrence of events, qualities, and processes, and the characteristic behaviors of various individuals, are contingent on the organization of spatio-temporally located bodies, whose internal structures and external relations determine and limit the appearance and disappearance of everything that

> happens. That this is so, is one of the best-tested conclusions of experience. . . . There is no place for the operation of disembodied forces, no place for an immaterial spirit directing the course of events, no place for the survival of personality after the corruption of the body which exhibits it.

The argument of this monograph shows that there is no scientific basis for those inferences. Natural bodies are unknown; scientific bodies exist in several different kinds of space and time; internal structures are below the threshold of observation; and external relations explain nothing. Certainly, external relations–as in the form of gravitation–do not determine the appearance or disappearance of anything; on the contrary, alleged appearances allegedly determine the law of gravitation.

Perhaps, for some philosophic reasons, a man may decide that the Leibnizian monads (those disembodied forces which make all things happen) are illusory; but there is no scientific argument to prove it.

Austin Farrer has said that no decent modern man can believe in creation eight thousand years ago. In reply, we ask, Can a scientist who is certain he has the truth, a scientist who has no room for belief because he either knows or he does not know (and if he knows there is no room for belief, and if he does not know he has no right to believe)–Can a scientist believe, know, or prove that the world has existed for more than twenty-four hours, or even five minutes? Scholars who, like Nagel, are so confident that God cannot possibly exist, and who, like Pearson, claim to make absolute judgments that are beyond all doubt, ought to be able scientifically to demonstrate with absolute certainty that the world has existed more than five minutes. That it has not, may seem to be a most absurd supposition. But if so absurd, can it not the more easily be put beyond all doubt? What then is the scientific argument against the proposition that just one minute ago the universe sprang into being, trees complete with rings, human beings with navels, and scientists with those ideas we call memories? At any rate, I cannot imagine any empirical observation that contradicts this exceedingly peculiar hypothesis. To dispose of it, something other than science is needed.

Much less can physics demonstrate the non-existence of a Supreme Intelligence who did what gravitation could not do and who directs the whole universe for his own purposes. And how laboratory procedure–confined in the nineteenth century to impossibly ideal conditions in the here and now, and in the twentieth barred from all descriptive application to reality–can show that personality does not survive death in a future life is utterly unintelligible.

Finally, to show the uselessness of science outside its own restricted sphere, science cannot determine its own value. No doubt, science enables man to dominate nature. By science, bombs are made and cancer may soon be cured. Most people think that bombs and medicine are good to have. But there is no experiment that proves their goodness. They are undoubtedly "good for" something; they are effective means to an end. But can experimentation demonstrate that either the destruction of cities or the extension of life is good?

The value of science depends on the value of life; but the value of life, when suicide is a possible choice, and therefore the value of science itself, must be determined by some sort of general philosophy, of which science is neither the whole nor the base, but only a subsidiary part. And it is my conviction that the best general philosophy, indeed the only position that satisfactorily manages all these problems, is the revelational philosophy of Christian theism.

POSTSCRIPT

*THE LIMITS AND USES OF SCIENCE**

Most Christians, when they think about science, have in mind some immediate apologetic interests. For example, mechanistic philosophy denies the occurrence of miracles and questions the value of prayer. Ordinary Christians then want an argument to justify prayer and miracles. Or, again, behaviorism has elaborated a theory of human nature that undermines the biblical concept of sin and has led many college students to gross immorality. Devout Christians naturally want some defense against Sigmund Freud, Bertrand Russell, and John Dewey. And underlying behaviorism is the theory of evolution that derives all life from inanimate matter and human life from the lower animals. Once again we want to view man, not as a mere sensory animal, but as a rational soul who looks forward to a life beyond the grave.

Though most Christians think about these matters in a haphazard sort of way, it is clear that physics, psychology, and zoology are technical subjects in which haphazard and desultory thought is of no value. Scholars must make these sciences their professional concern and devote their lives to their technical formulations. Some extremely devout students, however, viewing with concern the apostasy of the churches,

* Reprinted with permission from *Horizons of Science,* Carl F. H. Henry, ed., Harper and Row, 1978.

the secularism of the populace, and the universal rise in crime, drug addiction, and terrorism, now question whether a life of scientific research is worthwhile or even permissible for a Christian. Adults midway through their careers pay little attention to this question, but for a small number of gifted students, science as a vocational alternative is a forced and momentous option. The present essay, though chiefly interested in the nature and philosophy of science as such, permits itself, because of some current developments, to begin with the personal problem.

Every student must choose a life work. The problem is a real one. But Christian students may face the alternative of preaching the Gospel or doing physics. They are not likely to deny that the Bible approves of every method of making a living except those that are sinful. There are many occupations; and not every Christian, however sincere, is obligated to enter the ministry. Science is therefore a legitimate vocation.

On the other hand, in the present state of affairs, the world at large holds science in such high regard that some Christians have begun to question the value of preaching the Gospel. They have begun to share in the idolatry of science. Since they are professing Christians, reared in evangelical homes, retaining an attachment to biblical views, these theologian-philosophers have picked out Genesis 1:28, coined the phrase "cultural mandate," and so emphasized subduing the Earth for man's comfort, that the ministry has actually been downgraded. Some have gone so far as to suggest that the preaching of the Gospel should cease until society has been reconstructed along socialist lines and thus made ready to accept Christianity.

In prediluvian days, this cultural mandate of Genesis was fulfilled by the development of agriculture, the domestication of animals, the invention of musical instruments, metallurgy, and the rudimentary arts of war. These were scientific advances–scientific, at least, in the sense that science had to begin in this way–but they were made, so the record tells us, mainly by the ungodly line of Cain rather than by the descendants of Seth. Later on, as noted in Exodus 31, some of the godly line were skilled in art, if not in science.

Scripture thus approves of arts and sciences. But it does not approve of physical research to the exclusion of other worthy occupations. Approval admits of, and in this case requires, a recognition of degrees of importance. In fact, the Old Testament shows little interest in mathematics and physics, while it assigns a continuing role to the priests and Levites. And in the New Testament, if Paul had considered fulfillment of the cultural mandate a prerequisite for the execution of the "great commission," Christianity would never have gone beyond the boundaries of Palestine. All the less does the cultural mandate now need emphasis, because, with the special help of the ungodly line, it has been much more fully obeyed than the great commission.

It should also be noted that there is a large logical gap between the simple words of Genesis and some current proposals made under their aegis. If anyone appeals to Scripture for a cultural mandate, he must also show, for example, that the precise policies of Christian Labor Association of Canada (CLAC), the devaluation of currency, the requirement that small businesses with only four or five employees should make lengthy quarterly reports in quintuplicate, the law against elderly people with arthritis in their fingers that prevents them getting medicine in easily opened bottles, and volumes of irritating regulations are deducible by valid syllogisms from, not Genesis, but other parts of the Bible. Otherwise, however, science is an indubitably legitimate occupation for a college graduate.

So much for personal concerns. Science is both legitimate

and important, as well as real and pervasive. This judgment, however, raises the question, What is science? What is the nature and function of laboratory experimentation? Does it, by valid syllogisms, support a mechanistic world view, banish God from the universe, and reduce prayer to meditation on other subjects?

Such questions are indeed matters of apologetic interest, but the answers come only through technical philosophic analysis. Unfortunately, a short essay such as this can cover only a little ground. Therefore behaviorism, evolution, and much else have to be omitted in order to concentrate on one subject–physics–in more depth. This limitation can be justified somewhat because biology depends on physics, and the varying views of basic science profoundly alter all the dependent disciplines. Therefore, after a brief description of a few historical developments, the analysis of laboratory procedure and of the formulation of physical laws will lead to the conclusions here proposed.

Since the historical survey must also be brief, there is no point in peering into the pre-Newtonian era. Using the work of Galileo and Kepler, Sir Isaac Newton laid down principles that guided scientific advance for two centuries. From 1686 (or as soon thereafter as scientists could read the *Principia Mathematica)* to approximately 1900, all physics was based on certain definitions and basic laws, of which the following examples are especially important.

> Absolute, true, and mathematical time, of itself, and from its own nature, flows equably without relation to anything external. . . .
>
> Absolute space, in its own nature, without relation to anything external, remains always similar and immovable. . . .

> Absolute motion is the translation of a body from one absolute place into another. . . .
>
> Every body continues in its state of rest, or of uniform motion in a right line, unless it is compelled to change that state by forces impressed upon it.*

On these premises, Newton, with incredible genius and infinite patience, worked out his gravitational system in extensive detail. Yet, though his triumph was overwhelming, today his edifice lies in ruins. Nothing of it remains. Both its development and its demise shed light on the nature and compass of science.

During Newton's lifetime, Leibniz argued that the *Principia* depended on a set of contradictions. But other scientists were not impressed by objections from such armchair philosophers; they steadily built up the Newtonian theory in its many subordinate laws. Then two centuries later, Ernst Mach, quite innocent of Leibnizian scholarship, rediscovered Newton's logical blunder: The law of gravitation and the concepts of absolute time and motion cannot be combined. As Hans Reichenbach has written:

> The famous correspondence between Leibniz and Clarke . . . reads as though Leibniz had taken his arguments from expositions of Einstein's theory. . . . This conception of relativity was carried on at a later time by Ernst Mach, [who argued] . . . that a relativity of rotational motion requires an extension of relativism to the concept of inertial force.†

* A. Motte, trans., and F. Cajori, ed., *Mathematical Principles of Natural Phdosophy* (Berkeley: University of California Press, 1946).

† Hans Reichenbach, "The Philosophical Significance of the Theory of Relativity," in *Albert Einstein Philosopher-Scientist* Paul A. Schilpp, ed. (New York: Tudor Publishing Company, 1949), 299ff. Compare also Reichenbach, *Die Beweglehre bei Newton Leibniz und Huyghens* (Kanstudien, 1924), and *Philosophic Foundation of Quantum Mechanics, 1944.*

The relevant technical material is available to anyone who wishes to read it. Here it must suffice to indicate only two of Newton's difficulties. First, the idea that an absolute time flows equably without relation to anything external is scientifically useless and philosophically impossible. The reason is as follows. When we measure the motion of an auto, we say it goes at fifty miles an hour, that is, a certain distance in a certain time. But if time itself flows equably past us, this motion of time could not be measured by time–as the motion of the auto is measured by time–but only by its relation to some "supertime." Now, if time can be measured in seconds, and the motion of a car by feet per second, at what speed is the equable flow of time? Seconds per what? The auto goes at *feet per second;* time goes at *seconds* per what? After providing this answer, one must proceed and ask whether this "supertime" also flows equably. And so on *ad infinitum.*

A second difficulty with Newtonian theory concerns the principle of motion in a straight line. An empirical method for identifying straight-line motion in absolute space is impossible. The scientist would need, in addition to the present location of the moving body, a fixed point in space toward which the body was moving. A fixed star would satisfy this requirement. But there are no fixed stars. Hence the concept of motion in a straight line is useless in science.

Note too that the law of gravitation conflicts with the observed distribution of the star population. Gravitation implies a center to the universe where there are more stars per cubic volume than elsewhere, with the star population gradually decreasing from the center to a distant area of complete emptiness. However, actual observation does not bear out this hypothesis.

At this point, the non-scientific reader may want another reference to apologetics. Three can be given. First, the hypothesis of Newtonian mechanism–by which W. K. Clifford, Karl

Pearson, and others denounced miracles, has no experimental proof. Scientists may, and some do, remain mechanists, but they have no scientific basis for doing so. Hence there is no valid scientific argument against miracles.

Second, if the majestic Newtonian system has crumbled, and if science must always be tentative, no future synthesis can be taken as true and final. Everyone knows that physics has undergone immense changes. But even some scientists find it difficult to grasp this immensity. For instance, in *The Limitations of Science,* J. W. N. Sullivan tells an absorbing tale of the advancement and difficulties of contemporary science. But although he details the difficulties, sets forth the limitations, and verges on skepticism, he cannot quite bring himself to admit that science will always remain tentative.* Yet his own evidence is conclusive. So rapid and so extensive have been the changes in physics since the abolition of ether and the invention of wavicles that one may confidently affirm that, whereas Newtonianism lasted for two centuries, no theory today seems likely to last two decades. The arguments of this chapter refer to physics directly; but if physics is always tentative and never final, can the dependent sciences be superior? Clearly not. Therefore anti-Christian arguments based on science always depend on premises that will soon be discarded.

There is also a third point, or at least a confirmation of the second. The following analysis of laboratory procedure will show why no law of physics ever has been or ever can be a true description of natural processes.

On the assumption that the concepts of absolute space and time are discredited, and that the law of gravitation has fallen before the onslaught of relativity, it is pertinent to contrast the

* J. W. N. Sullivan, *The Limitations of Science* (New York: Viking Press, 1933; 1957). Compare also Henri Poincaré, *Science et Methode* (Paris: Flammarion, 1927), and its two succeeding volumes.

twentieth-century view of science as tentative with the nineteenth-century view that physics arrives at absolute truth. The general populace, even though dimly aware of the great scientific advances of this century, still retains the Newtonian optimism that science really discovers truth. On the opposite side, some professional scientists know so much up-to-date science, and so little history, that they doubt there ever was a theory of fixed truth in physics. There was such a theory, however. Its exponents are not straw men.*

Karl Pearson, in his *Grammar of Science,* taught that "the classification of facts and the formation of absolute judgments upon the basis of this classification–judgments independent of the idiosyncrasies of the individual mind–essentially sum up *the aim and method of modern science.*" That the absolute judgments of science extend to theology and ethics Pearson asserted explicitly:

> The goal of science is clear–it is nothing short of the complete interpretation of the universe. . . . Science does much more than demand that it shall be left in undisturbed possession of what the theologian and metaphysician please to term its "legitimate field." It claims that the whole range of phenomena, mental as well as physical–the entire universe–is its field. It asserts that the scientific method is the sole gateway to the whole region of knowledge.†

Professor A. J. Carlson wrote:

> What is the method of science? In essence it is this–the rejection *in toto* of all non-observational and

* W. K. Clifford, *The Common Sense of the Exact Sciences* (New York: Knopf, 1946); Karl Pearson, *Grammar of Science* (New York: Macmillan, 1911), 6, 14, 24; A. J. Carlson, "Science and the Supernatural," *Science:* 73 (1931): 217-225; reprinted in *The Scientific Monthly: 59* (1944): 85-95.

† Pearson, *Grammar of Science,* 6, 14, 24.

> non-experimental authority in the field of experience. . . . When no evidence is produced [in favor of a pronouncement] other than personal dicta, past and present "revelations" in dreams, or the "voice of God," the scientist can pay no attention whatsoever, except to ask, How do they get that way?

Carlson then confidently asserts: "The scientist tries to rid himself of all faiths and beliefs. He either knows or he does not know. If he knows, there is no room for faith or belief. If he does not know, he has no right to faith or belief."*

Even Hans Reichenbach, who, as the earlier quotation shows, ought to know better, succumbs to excessive optimism. In his *Modern Philosophy of Science,* he contrasts the perennial inability of philosophers to agree on anything with the common ground, universally recognized, which science has developed. A science teacher can teach "with the proud feeling of introducing his students into a realm of well-established truth." The results of science are "established with a superpersonal validity and universally accepted."†

Philipp Frank, on the other hand, more accurately represents the contemporary state of affairs: "It took a long time for the present day theory of motion to develop, and we do not know whether or not it is the right scheme for the future."‡

At this point it is instructive to note how backward are many liberal theologians. Rudolf Bultmann, for instance, asserts in *Kerygma and Myth* that "now that the forces and laws of nature have [really] been discovered, we can no longer believe in spirits, whether good or evil."** If he were consistent, Bultmann should

* A. J. Carlson, "Science and the Supernatural."

† Hans Reichenbach, *Modern Phdosophy of Science* (London: Routledge and Paul, 1959), 136, 149.

‡ Philipp Frank, *Philosophy of Science* (Englewood Cliffs, NJ.: Prentice-Hall, 1962), 90.

** Rudolf Bultmann, *Kerygma and Myth* (New York: Harper & Brothers, 1961), 4.

deny the existence of God, for God is a good spirit; but he seems to be not quite that consistent. And then in *Jesus Christ and Mythology,* he borrows from Auguste Comte and asserts that although science may change in some details, its methods of thinking will never change again.* He goes even further and seems to suggest that, whereas geocentric and heliocentric astronomy may continue to change, the (Newtonian?) laws of motion are immutable truths.

To support the previous assertion that physics can never discover or formulate a true description of natural processes, it is proper now to continue with a technical, albeit simple, analysis of laboratory methodology. What a scientist does, what he must do, prevents him from ever discovering the truth–the allegedly fixed, absolute truth of Clifford, Pearson, and Carlson, the unalterable law, final and irreplaceable.

After choosing a problem and starting an experiment pertinent to his hypothesis, the scientist soon takes a measurement. In fact, one may say that every experiment reduces to measuring the length of a line. It may be the length of mercury in a tube, it may be a certain distance on a meter stick, or the distance between two points on a dial. This reading the scientist records. Then he repeats the experiment and makes a second reading. Why? One possible reason for the second reading is that his eyes may have blinked the first time. They may, of course, blink the second time too, but the scientist hopes that a large number of readings will minimize these defects. But there is also another reason for making a second or a twenty-second reading. It may be that the mercury or the steel dial is palpitating, constantly expanding and contracting in the universal flux. A metal bar may not expand uniformly at all temperatures, nor at all times, even within very narrow

* Rudolf Bultmann, *Jesus Christ and Mythology* (New York: Scribners, 1958), 36-38.

temperature limits. Worse yet (so far as truth in science is concerned), the very thing being measured may be vibrating as well. Can any experiment prove that a cubic centimeter of gold, water, or sulphur always maintains the same weight? The measurements always vary, and atomic weights are only averages. If these variations are haphazard, then fixed truth is impossible, not only because our eyes blink but also because the object itself is not fixed. Indeed, in recent years this latter view has been accepted by some scientists, as will shortly be explained.

Before discussing further the metaphysical indeterminism to which the last paragraph refers, let us consider whether the use of averages can cancel out the blinking of the eyes and so preserve the truth of physical laws. What the physicist does is to repeat an experiment many times and record a list of the divergent readings. Then he calculates their arithmetic mean. There are other averages he could use, but for no empirical reason the physicist prefers arithmetic mean. There are other non-observational factors that contribute to the physicist's findings. In fact, the physicist's findings are not findings at all. They are formulations. Several factors in the formulation of a law are completely without observational evidence, but for the moment it is enough to note that the physicist chooses one type of average from among others.

Next, each reading is subtracted from the arithmetic mean, and a mean of these deviations is calculated. This second mean is attached to the first and is called the variable error. At this point, the physicist has a long list of figures such as 17.03 ± .0007. He then repeats the experiment a tedious number of times and obtains a long list of figures similar to the one above.

To formulate his law, the physicist now transfers these values to graph paper, where they appear as small rectangles.

Through them, he draws a curve, determines an algebraic equation that will yield a corresponding curve, and announces this to the world as a law of physics.

To simplify the argument, let us suppose that the averages result in three spots on the graph paper that look as if they can be joined by a straight line. The scientist may then announce that the law is $x = y$ *or* $x = Cy$. This could mean that the pressure on the bottom of a vessel increases and decreases with the height of the liquid, or that temperature varies with the length of a column of mercury. However, these small rectangles can also be joined by a sine curve, in fact by an infinite number of sine curves, and even by any one of an infinite number of other curves.

That three areas, or even three points on a straight line, can be points on a sine curve is most easily demonstrated visually by drawing a straight line through such a curve. More reconditely, the equation $y = A \sin (bx \times c)$ can always pass through three points determined by $x = Cy$. But the two equations are by no means the same law in physics.

The patient reader may permit or skip a more complex example. Suppose a series of experiments yields several values to be plotted slightly above the x axis. To the eye, they too may look like a straight line. But they could be the asymptotic end of a hyperbola. Or, to take an actual case, the values could be the asymptotic end of the law of gravitation, which is not a hyperbola. But since these values are rectangular areas, they could be connected by the awkward equation

$$y = \frac{e^{-\frac{A}{x}}}{x} + \ln (Bx)\, e^{-Bx}$$

Or, to acknowledge that the laws of physics are chosen for aesthetic considerations, the same values can also be determined by the much prettier equation

$$y = \frac{e^{-\frac{A}{x}} - e^{-\frac{x}{A}}}{x}$$

To bring this into connection with gravitation, the last equation may be changed to

$$y = \frac{e^{-\frac{A}{x}} - e^{-\frac{x}{A}}}{x^2}$$

Here we have the crux of the controversy between collision or contact and action at a distance. Newton thought that two bodies approach each other, collide, and rebound. Action at a distance seemed to him a non-mechanical impossibility, about which he made his oft-quoted statement, *hypotheses non fingo* (I make no hypotheses). But there is no observational evidence that requires bodies to collide. The force of gravitation may increase until the distance between the two bodies is infinitesimal, at which point a force of repulsion sets in; the curve swoops down from a high point on the *y* axis to an equally great minus quantity. Hence, action at a distance as well as Newton's impressed forces are equally compatible with the empirical observations. Experimentation never discovers how nature works. Every law of physics is an equation and, if viewed as a description of natural processes, false. The law is indubitably unprovable; it may be called false because (even aside from the theory of indeterminism) from a strictly mechanistic view, the chance of selecting the true description from among all the laws observation allows is one in infinity, or zero.

In a conversation concerning the nature of ultimate reality, Chaim Tschernowitz quotes Einstein as saying: "We know nothing about it at all. Our knowledge is but the knowledge of school children. . . . We shall know a little more than we do now. But the real nature of things–that we shall never know, never."*

From this the further conclusion follows that science can never disprove the truth of Christianity. It can never prove or disprove any metaphysical or theological assertion.

Two instances of this negative conclusion are now to be explained; and then a statement must be made on the value or import of science, if it is always false.

The two instances of this negative conclusion aim to emphasize that no metaphysical or theological conclusion is possible. Though the argument has shown that science cannot assert mechanism, it equally follows that neither can science assert indeterminism. About 1930, Heisenberg convinced the world that if his experiments on particles used sufficient light to locate the object, its velocity could not be determined because the energy of the light itself affected the object. On the other hand, if the light were dim enough not to interfere with the velocity, the object could not be located. But from this admirable scientific work, Heisenberg went on to conclude that mechanism is false and indeterminism is true. This inference is invalid.† The scientist's inability to construct an experiment that can determine both velocity and position surely gives no information on the still unknown laws of infinitesimal particles. Or, for that matter, the scientist's inability leaves uncertain whether nature is constructed of particles at all or whether it is a continuum. The result is zero, neither positive nor negative.

Some Christian apologetes, although recognizing that this result destroys all scientific arguments against miracles, may

* *Reader's Digest* (August 1972), 28.

† For a technical discussion see C. T. Ruddick, "On the Contingency of Natural Law," *The Monist* (July 1932), 330-383.

still defend scientific mechanism because the second law of thermodynamics seems to prove the doctrine of a creation in the finite past and disprove the doctrine of the eternity of the universe. However, if it is impossible accurately to measure a line, and if a series of areas on a graph furnish an infinite number of equations from which to choose, the second law of thermodynamics, along with all the others, becomes tentative and false.

Suppose a scientist for the brief moment of his life stands on the ocean shore watching the ebbing tide. The water level drops three feet in twelve hours, or in twelve billion years. He concludes that the tide cannot have been ebbing from eternity, for if that were so the water would have reached its lowest level billions of years before he came to watch it. Of course, that the tide rises as well as ebbs is philosophically impossible; or is it?

Now, the thermodynamic scientist has watched some energy systems, few in number, and at most for the period of only a few lifetimes. He has seen the ebb, and, without ever having seen an incoming tide, has recorded some points on a graph. They look like a straight line, but a mathematician can as well connect them by that disturbing sine curve. The scientist lives in the age of ebb; in a future age, the energy differences will again increase.

Perhaps a simplified and artificial example will make it clearer how a series of numbers can accommodate a large, even infinite, variety of equations. Let us suppose that the first point is at 3, the second point at 9, and the third point at 19.* Now, suppose the experimentation had ended with the number 9. Experimentation must always end somewhere, for otherwise no

* Morris R. Cohen and Ernest Nagel furnish this example [*An Introduction to Logic and Scientific Method* (New York: Harcourt, Brace and Company, 1934), 209ff.], though Nagel in his later books rejects the implication of operationalism.

time would be left to formulate a law. If, then, the last experiment gave the number 9, the law could be, and–in view of the scientist's dislike for Rube Goldberg complications–would be $x = 3^n$. The first number is three, the second is three to the second power, and the third will be extrapolated on the graph and predicted as 27.

But in this example, the experimentation did not stop at 9. The scientist went on to his third average of 19. Hence, $x = 3^n$ is refuted. A new formula must be devised. Well, the scientist has an infinite number of choices, of which two are:

$$x = 2n^2 + 1 \qquad \text{and} \qquad x = \frac{n^3}{3} + \frac{1n}{3} - 1$$

This artificial example should convince everyone that in any scientific theorizing there are infinite possibilities for extrapolation. Every one of them describes the natural process equally well; that is, not one of them can be shown to be the true description. Hence, every law of physics must be false, for science is always tentative.

The general public, including conservative theologians, and some scientists may reject this essay's thesis in irrational disgust; but if they do not, they are sure to ask–and it is a legitimate question–If science is always false, what value can it possibly have? Science has done wonders. Even if the cure of cancer still eludes us, we have put men on the Moon. How could false laws have produced such marvels?

The answer is that a law need not be true in order to be useful. Scientific laws not universally recognized as false have often enough been very useful. For example, no contemporary astronomer accepts the geocentric theory of Ptolemy. Nevertheless, even after Copernicus stole his thunder from the heliocentric system of Aristarchus and Plato, the Ptolemaic system was still able to predict the positions of the planets with greater accuracy than the Copernican theory could; and hence Ptolemy's laws were more useful for whatever such predictions are useful for.

Similarly, the theory that electromagnetic fields exist is now denied by at least some scientists; but no one denies that this false theory greatly advanced the utilization of electricity.

To relieve the distress of those who tire of physics, another example–and a most interesting one–can be taken from zoology, or veterinary medicine. Last century, milk fever in cows was a fearful disease with ninety percent fatality. After the Franco-Prussian war, Pasteur proposed the germ theory of disease and cured cases of anthrax and rabies. Thereupon a brilliant veterinarian argued to himself: Germs cause disease; therefore, if I inject an antiseptic into the cows' udders and kill the germs, the cows will get well. He did so; the cows recovered; he published his findings; and mortality rapidly dropped from ninety to thirty percent. Then he and others argued, this further proves the truth of the germ theory of disease.

But one day a cow phoned her vet to come pronto or she would die. He immediately hitched up his Lincoln Continental and at 60 MPH (mud puddles per hedgerow) soon arrived on the scene. But then, when he opened his black satchel, he discovered that most unfortunately he had neglected to put in a supply of antiseptic. More fortunately, however, some cows still died; and since neither the cow nor the farmer could tell the difference, they would never know that he had injected distilled water instead of Lugol. To his surprise, the cow got well.

Being of a scientific mind, he continued to inject distilled water in other cows, with the result that as many or even more cows recovered. He too published his findings; and other inquisitive veterinarians tried compressed air, with even better results. What, then, of the germ theory of disease? Distilled water and compressed air do not kill germs.* The point is that the germ theory, now proved false with respect to milk fever, nevertheless was very useful in curing cows. Hence, the utility of science can be defended even while asserting its falsity.

Now, in conclusion: Science is forever incapable of producing a valid argument against the existence of God, the occurrence of a miracle, including a supernatural revelation, and a life beyond the grave. The author† of the article on "Atheism" in *The Encyclopedia of Philosophy* bases the arguments on the problem of evil; other writers may attempt to prove atheism on other bases. This article concerns physics; and physics–with its derivatives of chemistry and biology–is totally, totally, incompetent, both positively and negatively, to make any metaphysical or theological pronouncement. Science is always false, but often useful.

---

* The reader may check to see if milk fever is now cured by injections of calcium into the cow's neck.

† Paul Edwards, "Atheism," *The Encyclopedia of Philosophy,* The Free Press, 1967, Vol. I, 174-189.

Bibliography

Aristotle. *The Works of Aristotle.* Edited by W. D. Ross. Oxford University Press.

Benjamin, A. Cornelius. *Operationism.* C.C. Thomas, 1955.

Bergmann, Gustav. *Philosophy of Science.* University of Wisconsin Press, 1957.

Bridgman, Percy *The Logic of Modern Physics.* Macmillan, 1927.

—. *The Way Things Are.* Harvard University Press, 1959.

Büchner, Ludwig. *Force and Matter.* Peter Eckler, 1891.

Bultmann, Rudolf. *Kerygma and Myth.* Edited by Hans Werner Bartsch. Harper and Brothers, 1961.

—. *Jesus Christ and Mythology.* Scribners, 1958.

Burtt, Edwin A. *The Metaphysical Foundations of Modern Science.* Harcourt Brace and Co., 1925.

Butterfield, Herbert. *The Origins of Modern Science.* Macmillan, 1951.

Cabanis, P. J. S. *Rapports du physique et du moral de l'homme.* Paris, 1802.

Carlson, A. J. "Science and the Supernatural." *Science,* 73:217-225, 1931; and *The Scientific Monthly,* 59:85-95, 1944.

Churchman, C. West. *Theory of Experimental Inference.*

Clifford, W. K. *The Common Sense of the Exact Sciences.* A. A. Knopf, 1946.

Dampier-Whettham, W. C. D. A *History of Science.* The Macmillan Co., 1951.

Descartes, René. *Oeuvres de Descartes* (Principia Philosophiae). Adam et Tannery, J. Vrin, 1897-1913.

Duhem, Pierre. *Le Système du Monde.* Librairie Scientifique Hermann et cie., 1913.

Frank, Philipp. *Philosophy of Science.* Prentice-Hall, 1962.

Haeckel, Ernst. *The Riddle of the Universe.* Harper and Brothers, 1901.

Hall, A. R. *The Scientific Revolution.* Beacon Press, 1962.

Holbach, P. H. T Baron d'. *Le Christianisme devoile.* London, 1761.

La Mettrie, J. O. de. *Man a Machine.* Open Court, 1912.

Lange, F. W. *History of Materialism.* Harcourt Brace and Co., 1925.

Laplace, Pierre Simon. *Mecanique celeste.* Hillard, Gray, Little, and Wilkins, 1829-39.

Lindsay and Margenau. *Foundations of Physics.* J. Wiley and Sons, 1936.

Loeb, Jacques. *The Mechanistic Conception of Life.* University of Chicago Press, 1912.

Mach, Ernst. *Science of Mechanics.* Open Court, 1942.

Nagel, Ernest. *The Structure of Science.* Harcourt Brace and World, 1961.

Newton, Isaac. *Principia Mathematica.* Edited by Florian Cajori. University of California Press, 1934.

Pearson, Karl. *Grammar of Science.* Macmillan Co., 1911.

Reichenbach, Hans. *Modern Philosophy of Science.* Routledge and Kegan Paul, 1959.

Russell, Bertrand. *Mysticism and Logic.* Longmans Green and Company, 1925.

Sullivan, J. W. N. *The Limitations of Science.* The Viking Press, 1933.

INDEX

The Crisis of Our Time

Historians have christened the thirteenth century the Age of Faith and termed the eighteenth century the Age of Reason. The twentieth century has been called many things: the Atomic Age, the Age of Inflation, the Age of the Tyrant, the Age of Aquarius. But it deserves one name more than the others: the Age of Irrationalism. Contemporary secular intellectuals are anti-intellectual. Contemporary philosophers are anti-philosophy. Contemporary theologians are anti-theology.

In past centuries, secular philosophers have generally believed that knowledge is possible to man. Consequently they expended a great deal of thought and effort trying to justify knowledge. In the twentieth century, however, the optimism of the secular philosophers has all but disappeared. They despair of knowledge.

Like their secular counterparts, the great theologians and doctors of the church taught that knowledge is possible to man. Yet the theologians of the twentieth century have repudiated that belief. They also despair of knowledge. This radical skepticism has filtered down from the philosophers and theologians and penetrated our entire culture, from television to music to literature. *The Christian in the twentieth century is confronted with an overwhelming cultural consensus–sometimes stated explicitly but most often implicitly: Man does not and cannot know anything truly.*

What does this have to do with Christianity? Simply this: If man can know nothing truly, man can truly know nothing. We cannot know that the Bible is the Word of God, that Christ died for his people, or that Christ is alive today at the right hand of the Father. Unless knowledge is possible, Christianity is nonsensical, for it claims to be knowledge. What is at stake in the twentieth century is not simply a single doctrine, such as the virgin birth, or the existence of Hell, as important as those doctrines may be, but the whole of Christianity itself. If knowledge is not possible to man, it is worse than silly to argue points of doctrine–it is insane.

The irrationalism of the present age is so thoroughgoing and pervasive that even the Remnant–the segment of the professing church that remains faithful–has accepted much of it, frequently without even being aware of what it was accepting. In some circles this irrationalism has become synonymous with piety and humility, and those who oppose it are denounced as rationalists–as though to be logical were a sin. Our contemporary anti-theologians make a contradiction and call it a Mystery. The faithful ask for truth and are given Paradox. If any balk at swallowing the absurdities of the anti-theologians, they are frequently marked as heretics or schismatics who seek to act independently of God.

There is no greater threat facing the true church of Christ at this moment than the irrationalism that now controls our entire culture. Totalitarianism, guilty of tens of millions of murders–including those of millions of Christians–is to be feared, but not nearly so much as the idea that we do not and cannot know the truth. Hedonism, the popular philosophy of America, is not to be feared so much as the belief that logic–that "mere human logic," to use the religious irrationalists' own phrase–is futile. The attacks on truth, on revelation, on the intellect, and on logic are renewed daily. But note well: The misologists–the haters of logic–use logic to demonstrate the futility of using logic. The anti-intellectuals construct intricate intellectual arguments to prove the insufficiency of the intellect. The anti-theologians use the revealed Word of God to show that there can be no revealed Word of God–or that if there could, it would remain impenetrable darkness and Mystery to our finite minds.

Nonsense Has Come

Is it any wonder that the world is grasping at straws–the straws of experientialism, mysticism, and drugs? After all, if people are told that the Bible contains insoluble mysteries, then is not a flight into mysticism to be expected? On what grounds can it be condemned? Certainly not on logical grounds or Biblical grounds, if logic is futile and the Bible unintelligible. Moreover, if it cannot be condemned on logical or Biblical grounds, it cannot be condemned at all. If people are going to have a religion of the mysterious, they will not adopt Christianity: They will have a genuine mystery religion. "Those who call for Nonsense," C. S. Lewis once wrote, "will find that it comes." And that is precisely what has happened. The popularity of Eastern mysticism, of drugs, and of religious experience is the logical consequence of the irrationalism of the twentieth century. There can and will be no Christian reformation–and no reconstruction of society–unless and until the irrationalism of the age is totally repudiated by Christians.

The Church Defenseless

Yet how shall they do it? The spokesmen for Christianity

have been fatally infected with irrationalism. The seminaries, which annually train thousands of men to teach millions of Christians, are the finishing schools of irrationalism, completing the job begun by the government schools and colleges. Some of the pulpits of the most conservative churches (we are not speaking of the apostate churches) are occupied by graduates of the anti-theological schools. These products of modern anti-theological education, when asked to give a reason for the hope that is in them, can generally respond with only the intellectual analogue of a shrug–a mumble about Mystery. They have not grasped–and therefore cannot teach those for whom they are responsible–the first truth: "And you shall know the truth." Many, in fact, explicitly deny it, saying that, at best, we possess only "pointers" to the truth, or something "similar" to the truth, a mere analogy. Is the impotence of the Christian church a puzzle? Is the fascination with pentecostalism and faith healing among members of conservative churches an enigma? Not when one understands the sort of studied nonsense that is purveyed in the name of God in the seminaries.

The Trinity Foundation

The creators of The Trinity Foundation firmly believe that theology is too important to be left to the licensed theologians–the graduates of the schools of theology. They have created The Trinity Foundation for the express purpose of teaching the faithful all that the Scriptures contain–not warmed over, baptized, secular philosophies. Each member of the board of directors of The Trinity Foundation has signed this oath: "I believe that the Bible alone and the Bible in its entirety is the Word of God and, therefore, inerrant in the autographs. I believe that the system of truth presented in the Bible is best summarized in the Westminster Confession of Faith. So help me God."

The ministry of The Trinity Foundation is the presentation of the system of truth taught in Scripture as clearly and as completely as possible. We do not regard obscurity as a virtue, nor confusion as a sign of spirituality. Confusion, like all error, is sin, and teaching that confusion is all that Christians can hope for is doubly sin.

The presentation of the truth of Scripture necessarily involves the rejection of error. The Foundation has exposed and will continue to expose the irrationalism of the twentieth century, whether its current spokesman be an existentialist philosopher or a professed Reformed theologian. We oppose anti-intellectualism, whether it be espoused by a neo-orthodox theologian or a fundamentalist evangelist. We reject misology, whether it be on the lips of a neo-evangelical or those of a Roman Catholic charismatic. To each error we bring the brilliant light of Scripture, proving all things, and holding fast to that which is true.

The Primacy of Theory

The ministry of The Trinity Foundation is not a "practical" ministry. If you are a pastor, we will not enlighten you on how to organize an ecumenical prayer meeting in your community or how to double church attendance in a year. If you are a homemaker, you will have to read elsewhere to find out how to become a total woman. If you are a businessman, we will not tell you how to develop a social conscience. The professing church is drowning in such "practical" advice.

The Trinity Foundation is unapologetically theoretical in its outlook, believing that theory without practice is dead, and that practice without theory is blind. The trouble with the professing church is not primarily in its practice, but in its theory. Christians do not know, and many do not even care to know, the doctrines of Scripture. Doctrine is intellectual, and Christians are generally anti-intellectual. Doctrine is ivory tower philosophy, and they scorn ivory towers. The ivory tower, however, is the control tower of a civilization. It is a fundamental, theoretical mistake of the practical men to think that they can be merely practical, for practice is always the practice of some theory. The relationship between theory and practice is the relationship between cause and effect. If a person believes correct theory, his practice will tend to be correct. The practice of contemporary Christians is immoral because it is the practice of false theories. It is a major theoretical mistake of the practical men to think that they can ignore the ivory towers of the philosophers and theologians as irrelevant to their lives. Every action that the "practical" men take is governed by the thinking that has occurred in some ivory tower–whether that tower be the British Museum, the Academy, a home in Basel, Switzerland, or a tent in Israel.

In Understanding Be Men

It is the first duty of the Christian to understand correct theory–correct doctrine–and thereby implement correct practice. This order–first theory, then practice–is both logical and Biblical. It is, for example, exhibited in Paul's epistle to the Romans, in which he spends the first eleven chapters expounding theory and the last five discussing practice. The contemporary teachers of Christians have not only reversed the order, they have inverted the Pauline emphasis on theory and practice. The virtually complete failure of the teachers of the professing church to instruct the faithful in correct doctrine is the cause of the misconduct and cultural impotence of Christians. The church's lack of power is the result of its lack of truth. The *Gospel* is the power of God, not religious experience or personal relationship. The church has no power because it has abandoned the Gospel, the good news, for a religion of experientialism. Twentieth-century American Christians are children carried about by every wind of doctrine, not knowing what they believe, or even if they believe anything for certain.

The chief purpose of The Trinity Foundation is to counteract the irrationalism of the age and to expose the errors of the teachers of the church. Our emphasis–on the Bible as the sole source of truth, on the primacy of the intellect, on the supreme importance of correct doctrine, and on the necessity for systematic and logical thinking–is almost unique in Christendom. To the extent that the church survives–and she will survive and flourish–it will be because of her increasing acceptance of these basic ideas and their logical implications.

We believe that the Trinity Foundation is filling a vacuum in Christendom. We are saying that Christianity is intellectually defensible–that, in fact, it is the only intellectually defensible system of thought. We are saying that God has made the wisdom of this world–whether that wisdom be called science, religion, philosophy, or common sense–foolishness. We are appealing to all Christians who have not conceded defeat in the intellectual battle with the world to join us in our efforts to raise a standard to which all men of sound mind can repair.

The love of truth, of God's Word, has all but disappeared in our time. We are committed to and pray for a great instauration. But though we may not see this reformation of Christendom in our lifetimes, we believe it is our duty to present the whole counsel of God because Christ has commanded it. The results of our teaching are in God's hands, not ours. Whatever those results, his Word is never taught in vain, but always accomplishes the result that he intended it to accomplish. Professor Gordon H. Clark has stated our view well:

> There have been times in the history of God's people, for example, in the days of Jeremiah, when refreshing grace and widespread revival were not to be expected: The time was one of chastisement. If this twentieth century is of a similar nature, individual Christians here and there can find comfort and strength in a study of God's Word. But if God has decreed happier days for us and if we may expect a world-shaking and genuine spiritual awakening, then it is the author's belief that a zeal for souls, however necessary, is not the sufficient condition. Have there not been devout saints in every age, numerous enough to carry on a revival? Twelve such persons are plenty. What distinguishes the arid ages from the period of the Reformation, when nations were moved as they had not been since Paul preached in Ephesus, Corinth, and Rome, is the latter's fullness of knowledge of God's Word. To echo an early Reformation thought, when the ploughman and the garage attendant know the Bible as well as the theologian does, and know it better than some contemporary theologians, then the desired awakening shall have already occurred.

In addition to publishing books, the Foundation publishes a monthly newsletter, *The Trinity Review.* Subscriptions to *The Review* are free to U.S. addresses; please write to the address below to become a subscriber. If you would like further information or would like to join us in our work, please let us know.

The Trinity Foundation is a non-profit foundation, tax exempt under section 501 (c)(3) of the Internal Revenue Code of 1954. You can help us disseminate the Word of God through your tax-deductible contributions to the Foundation.

John W. Robbins

Intellectual Ammunition

The Trinity Foundation is committed to the reformation of philosophy and theology along Biblical lines. We regard God's command to bring all our thoughts into conformity with Christ very seriously, and the books listed below are designed to accomplish that goal. They are written with two subordinate purposes: (1) to demolish all secular claims to knowledge; and (2) to build a system of truth based upon the Bible alone.

Philosophy

Behaviorism and Christianity, Gordon H. Clark $6.95

Behaviorism *is a critique of both secular and religious behaviorists. It includes chapters on John Watson, Edgar S. Singer, Jr., Gilbert Ryle, B. F. Skinner, and Donald MacKay. Clark's refutation of behaviorism and his argument for a Christian doctrine of man are unanswerable.*

A Christian Philosophy of Education $8.95
Gordon H. Clark

The first edition of this book was published in 1946. It sparked the contemporary interest in Christian schools. Dr. Clark thoroughly revised and updated it, and it is needed now more than ever. Its chapters include: The Need for a World-View, The Christian World-View, The Alternative to Christian Theism, Neutrality, Ethics, The Christian Philosophy of Education, Academic Matters, Kindergarten to University. Three appendices are included as well: The Relationship of Public Education to Christianity, A Protestant World-View, and Art and the Gospel.

A Christian View of Men and Things $10.95
Gordon H. Clark

No other book achieves what A Christian View *does: the presentation of Christianity as it applies to history, politics, ethics, science, religion, and epistemology. Clark's command of both worldly philosophy and Scripture is evident on every page, and the result is a breathtaking and invigorating challenge to the wisdom of this world.*

Clark Speaks From The Grave, Gordon H. Clark $3.95

Dr. Clark chides some of his critics for their failure to defend Christianity competently. Clark Speaks *is a stimulating and illuminating discussion of the errors of contemporary apologists.*

Education, Christianity, and the State $9.95
J. Gresham Machen
Edited by John W. Robbins

Machen was one of the foremost educators, theologians, and defenders of Christianity in the twentieth century. The author of numerous scholarly books, Machen saw clearly that if Christianity is to survive and flourish, a system of Christian schools must be established. This collection of essays and speeches captures his thoughts on education over nearly three decades.

Essays on Ethics and Politics, Gordon H. Clark $10.95

Clark's essays, written over the course of five decades, are a major statement of Christian ethics.

Gordon H. Clark: Personal Recollections $6.95
John W. Robbins, editor

Friends of Dr. Clark have written their recollections of the man. Contributors include family members, colleagues, students, and friends such as Harold Lindsell, Carl Henry, Ronald Nash, Dwight Zeller, and Joseph Pattison. The book includes an extensive bibliography of Clark's work.

Historiography: Secular and Religious $13.95
Gordon H. Clark

In this masterful work, Clark applies his philosophy to the writing of history, examining all the major schools of historiography.

An Introduction to Christian Philosophy $8.95
Gordon H. Clark

In 1966 Clark delivered three lectures on philosophy at Wheaton College. In these lectures he criticizes secular philosophy and launches a philosophical revolution in the name of Christ.

Language and Theology, Gordon H. Clark $9.95

There are two main currents in twentieth-century philosophy–language philosophy and existentialism. Both are hostile to Christianity. Clark disposes of language philosophy in this brilliant critique of Bertrand Russell, Ludwig Wittgenstein, Rudolf Carnap, A. J. Ayer, Langdon Gilkey, and many others.

Logic, Gordon H. Clark $8.95

Written as a textbook for Christian schools, Logic *is another unique book from Clark's pen. His presentation of the laws of thought, which must be followed if Scripture is to be understood correctly, and which are found in Scripture itself, is both clear and thorough.* Logic *is an indispensable book for the thinking Christian.*

Logic Workbook, Elihu Carranza $11.95

Designed to be used in conjunction with Clark's textbook Logic, *this* Workbook *contains hundreds of exercises and test questions on perforated pages for ease of use by students.*

Logic Workbook Answer Key, Elihu Carranza $2.95

The Key *contains answers to all the exercises and tests in the* Workbook.

Lord God of Truth, Concerning the Teacher $7.95
Gordon H. Clark and Aurelius Augustine

This essay by Clark summarizes many of the most telling arguments against empiricism and defends the Biblical teaching that we know God and truth immediately. The dialogue by Augustine is a refutation of empirical language philosophy.

The Philosophy of Science and Belief in God $8.95
Gordon H. Clark

In opposing the contemporary idolatry of science, Clark analyzes three major aspects of science: the problem of motion, Newtonian science, and modern theories of physics. His conclusion is that science, while it may be useful, is always false; and he demonstrates its falsity in numerous ways. Since science is always false, it can offer no objection to the Bible and Christianity.

Religion, Reason and Revelation $10.95
Gordon H. Clark

One of Clark's apologetical masterpieces, Religion, Reason and Revelation *has been praised for the clarity of its thought and language. It includes chapters on Is Christianity a Religion? Faith and Reason, Inspiration and Language, Revelation and Morality, and God and Evil. It is must reading for all serious Christians.*

Thales to Dewey: A History of Philosophy $18.95
Gordon H. Clark

This is the best one-volume history of philosophy in English.

Three Types of Religious Philosophy $6.95
Gordon H. Clark

In this book on apologetics, Clark examines empiricism, rationalism, dogmatism, and contemporary irrationalism, which does not rise to the level of philosophy. He offers a solution to the question, "How can Christianity be defended before the world?"

William James and John Dewey $8.95
Gordon H. Clark

William James and John Dewey are two of the most influential philosophers America has produced. Their philosophies of instrumentalism and pragmatism are hostile to Christianity, and Clark demolishes their arguments.

Theology

The Atonement, Gordon H. Clark $8.95

In The Atonement, *Clark discusses the covenants, the virgin birth and incarnation, federal headship and representation, the relationship between God's sovereignty and justice, and much more. He analyzes traditional views of the atonement and criticizes them in the light of Scripture alone.*

The Biblical Doctrine of Man, Gordon H. Clark $6.95

Is man soul and body or soul, spirit, and body? What is the image of God? Is Adam's sin imputed to his children? Is evolution true? Are men totally depraved? What is the heart? These are some of the questions discussed and answered from Scripture in this book.

The Clark–Van Til Controversy $7.95
Herman Hoeksema

This collection of essays by the founder of the Protestant Reformed Church–essays written at the time of the Clark–Van Til controversy–is one of the best commentaries on the events in print.

Cornelius Van Til: The Man and The Myth $2.45
John W. Robbins

The actual teachings of this eminent Philadelphia theologian have been obscured by the myths that surround him. This book penetrates those myths and criticizes Van Til's surprisingly unorthodox views of God and the Bible.

The Everlasting Righteousness, Horatius Bonar $8.95

Originally published in 1874, the language of Bonar's masterpiece on justification by faith alone has been updated and Americanized for easy reading and clear understanding. This is one of the best books ever written on justification.

Faith and Saving Faith, Gordon H. Clark $6.95

The views of the Roman Catholic church, John Calvin, Thomas Manton, John Owen, Charles Hodge, and B. B. Warfield are discussed in this book. Is the object of faith a person or a proposition? Is faith more than belief? Is belief more than thinking with assent, as Augustine said? In a world chaotic with differing views of faith, Clark clearly explains the Biblical view of faith and saving faith.

God and Evil, Gordon H. Clark $4.95

This volume is Chapter 5 of Religion, Reason and Revelation, *in which Clark presents his solution to the problem of evil.*

God's Hammer: The Bible and Its Critics $10.95
Gordon H. Clark
Edited by John W. Robbins

The starting point of Christianity, the doctrine on which all other doctrines depend, is "The Bible alone, and the Bible in its entirety, is the Word of God written, and therefore inerrant in the autographs." Over the centuries the opponents of Christianity, with Satanic shrewdness, have concentrated their attacks on the truthfulness and completeness of the Bible. In the twentieth century the attack is not so much in the fields of history and archaeology as in philosophy. Clark's brilliant defense of the complete truthfulness of the Bible is captured in this collection of eleven major essays.

Guide to the Westminster Confession and Catechism
James E. Bordwine $13.95

This large book contains the full text of both the Westminster Confession (both original and American versions) and the Larger Catechism. In addition, it offers a chapter-by-chapter summary of the Confession and a unique index to both the Confession and the Catechism.

The Holy Spirit, Gordon H. Clark $8.95

This discussion of the third person of the Trinity is both concise and exact. Clark includes chapters on the work of the Spirit, sanctification, and Pentecostalism. This book is part of his multi-volume systematic theology that began appearing in print in 1985.

The Incarnation, Gordon H. Clark $8.95

Who is Christ? The attack on the incarnation in the nineteenth and twentieth centuries has been vigorous, but the orthodox response has been lame. Clark reconstructs the doctrine of the incarnation, building and improving upon the Chalcedonian definition.

In Defense of Theology, Gordon H. Clark $9.95

There are four groups to whom Clark addresses this book: average Christians who are uninterested in theology, atheists and agnostics, religious experientialists, and serious Christians. The vindication of the knowledge of God against the objections of three of these groups is the first step in theology.

The Johannine Logos, Gordon H. Clark $5.95

Clark analyzes the relationship between Christ, who is the truth, and the Bible. He explains why John used the same word to refer to both Christ and his teaching. Chapters deal with the Prologue to John's Gospel, Logos and Rheemata, Truth, and Saving Faith.

Justification by Faith Alone, Charles Hodge $10.95
Edited by John W. Robbins

Charles Hodge of Princeton Seminary was the best American theologian of the nineteenth century. Here in one volume are his two major essays on justification. This book is essential in defending the faith.

Predestination, Gordon H. Clark $8.95

Clark thoroughly discusses one of the most controversial and pervasive doctrines of the Bible: that God is, quite literally, Almighty. Free will, the origin of evil, God's omniscience, creation, and the new birth are all presented within a Scriptural framework. The objections of those who do not believe in the Almighty God are considered and refuted. This edition also contains the text of the booklet, Predestination in the Old Testament.

Sanctification, Gordon H. Clark $8.95

In this book, which is part of Clark's multi-volume systematic theology, he discusses historical theories of sanctification, the sacraments, and the Biblical doctrine of sanctification.

Study Guide to the Westminster Confession $10.95
W. Gary Crampton

This Study Guide *may be used by individuals or classes. It contains a paragraph by paragraph summary of the Westminster Confession, and questions for the student to answer. Space for answers is provided. The* Guide *will be most beneficial when used in conjunction with Clark's* What Do Presbyterians Believe?

Today's Evangelism: Counterfeit or Genuine? $6.95
Gordon H. Clark

Clark compares the methods and messages of today's evangelists with Scripture, and finds that Christianity is on the wane because the Gospel has been distorted or lost. This is an extremely useful and enlightening book.

The Trinity, Gordon H. Clark $8.95

Apart from the doctrine of Scripture, no teaching of the Bible is more important than the doctrine of God. Clark's defense of the orthodox doctrine of the Trinity is a principal portion of Clark's systematic theology. There are chapters on the deity of Christ, Augustine, the incomprehensibility of God, Bavinck and Van Til, and the Holy Spirit, among others.

What Calvin Says, W. Gary Crampton $7.95

This is both a readable and thorough introduction to the theology of John Calvin.

What Do Presbyterians Believe? Gordon H. Clark $8.95

This classic introduction to Christian doctrine has been republished. It is the best commentary on the Westminster Confession of Faith that has ever been written. A Study Guide *is now available for it.*

Commentaries on the New Testament

Colossians, Gordon H. Clark $ 6.95
Ephesians, Gordon H. Clark $ 8.95
First Corinthians, Gordon H. Clark $10.95
First John, Gordon H. Clark $10.95
First and Second Thessalonians, Gordon H. Clark $ 5.95
New Heavens, New Earth (First and Second Peter)
Gordon H. Clark $10.95
The Pastoral Epistles (I and II Timothy and Titus)
Gordon H. Clark $ 9.95
Philippians, Gordon H. Clark $ 9.95

All of Clark's commentaries are expository, not technical, and are written for the Christian layman. His purpose is to explain the text clearly and accurately so that the Word of God will be thoroughly known by every Christian.

The Trinity Library

We will send you one copy of each of the 48 books listed above for $325. You may also order the books you want individually on the order blank on the next page. Because some of the books are in short supply, we must reserve the right to substitute others of equal or greater value in The Trinity Library. This special offer expires June 30, 2000.

Order Form

Name ____

Address ______________________________________

____

____

Please:

- ☐ add my name to the mailing list for *The Trinity Review.* I understand that there is no charge for the *Review* sent to a U.S. address.
- ☐ accept my tax deductible contribution of $______ for the work of the Foundation.
- ☐ send me___copies of *The Philosophy of Science and Belief in God.* I enclose as payment $ _________.
- ☐ send me the Trinity Library of 48 books. I enclose US$325 as full payment.
- ☐ send me the following books. I enclose full payment in the amount of $____________ for them.

____

____

____

____

Mail to:

The Trinity Foundation
Post Office Box 1666, Hobbs, New Mexico 88240
United States of America

Please add $1.00 for postage on orders less than $10. For foreign orders, please enclose 20 percent of the total value of the books ordered. Thank you. For quantity discounts, please write to the Foundation.

